# INVENT, INNOVATE & PROSPER

# INVENT, INNOVATE & PROSPER

A Step-by-Step Guide to Successful Inventing

MICHAEL G. COLBURN

Inventor, Entrepreneur,
Founder of Ideas Well Done, LLC

Inventing Pathways Publishing

Inventing Pathways Publishing LLC
152 Deforest Road
Burlington, Vermont 05401





ISBN: 978-1733770804
eISBN: 978-1733770811



Library of Congress Control Number: 2019903103

Developmental editor: Maria Gagliano
Copy editor: Jennifer Eck
Reader: Andi Cumbo-Floyd
Permissions and Citations: Kelly Figueroa-Ray, Copy Write Consultants (CWC)
Interior designer: Pauline Neuwirth, Neuwirth & Associates, Inc.
Cover designer: Zoe Norvell

# Contents

# Dedication

**TO MY WIFE,** Mary Esther, who is my life partner and a partner in every adventure we undertake, thank you for your love and support. I love and support you back.

To the other deeply cherished loves of my life, my daughter, Lissa, and incredible granddaughter, Kaleigh

In memoriam my first wife, Linda

You have all added so much to my life. Thank you.

Thank you, Steve Bogner (Ideas Well Done) and Todd Guyette (Colburn & Guyette Consulting Partners) for the years of dedicated work and for carrying on the business adventures.

Mike

# Introduction

**INVENTIONS DON'T JUST** happen in the minds of geniuses or the gifted; anyone who creates a unique solution to a problem can be an inventor. Some of the most successful inventions tackled little problems with simple solutions that generated huge financial returns for their creators. Later I'll share the story of one device costing less than a penny to produce that has generated revenue beyond calculation and currently sells over 14 million units a day.

Some inventions seem like pure luck, but the truth is that most are the result of an applied creation process that the inventor executed, whether intentionally or by instinct.

The same inventive processes can create innovations in business, new art or music, new curricula for education, a new recipe, or a new manuscript such as this one. I wrote this book to show you how you can take this process and apply it to your own goals.

I am an inventor. I wasn't always, but I made myself into one. I spent the better part of four decades in entrepreneurial ventures based on my creative efforts. I taught myself the techniques and processes for creating things that have never existed before. I set upon a quest to learn from those who had succeeded as inventors before me. I found that many successful creators' techniques followed similar patterns; I even found references in literature to similar processes used to solve crimes and in science to discover unknown data. In crime-solving, for example, making detailed observations is critical to a successful outcome. Observation also plays a huge role in inventing. In science, new discoveries are often a result of an individual's hypothesis, which is then proven or disproved; again this is an important process in inventing. From literature, Sir Arthur Conan Doyle and his character Sherlock Holmes had much to offer to the study of inventive process, so I have sprinkled a visit to the famous detective throughout this book. I hope you enjoy the connections.

You have probably applied some of the invention process steps in your schooling, occupation, artistic endeavors, business, or even cooking or sports. What we'll explore is how to recognize and apply the talents you have in a logical step-by-step creation process that is directed to inventing.

I founded a design and consulting firm, which I ran for 19 years, planning and designing commercial food service facilities all over the world. Our clients included universities, embassies and governments of multiple nations, schools, hospitals, military cities, restaurants, and even projects for royalty. We started each project by exploring the client's needs and then thinking through solutions that addressed the project's challenges. That alone wasn't invention, but it provided a good foundation when starting with blank sheets of paper (or yellow tracing paper in those days) and creating something entirely new. Exploring clients' needs and defining objectives (or problems to overcome) is akin to the initial steps in inventing; we'll explore identifying problems to solve and defining goals as initial steps in the invention creation process.

My first real product invention came because of a mistake. We had designed a rooftop restaurant as part of an office building project in Baghdad. The construction documents that the owner provided to the architect included a list of specialty equipment needed to execute the planned menu. We used this document as a guide to design the facility and provide the necessary layouts, fabrication designs, utility requirements, and purchasing documents. I received a call one day near completion of the construction from a very angry Chinese construction manager in Baghdad who was overseeing the work. With a heavy accent he yelled something like "camacook miss." I finally calmed him down to interpret his complaint and then retrieved our design program from the files. Comparing the design specification and our plans and schedules I found that in fact there was a piece of equipment missing. It seems that we had missed the need for a "camel cooker" (perhaps we thought it a joke). Eventually I said I would have to call him back and we arranged a call for the next evening. I had no idea they cooked camels let alone had equipment to do so. We scanned all our sources but didn't find any cooking device of the sort. I had to admit our mistake to the construction manager and ask, "What size camel do you want to cook?" In two days, we designed a motor-driven vertical-chain spit in a stainless-steel box lined with radiant heating elements to cook a quarter camel. We sent the plan off to have the piece fabricated locally in Baghdad. No patent, total of one built, and not a real invention perhaps, but an embodiment of solving a problem with a unique and useful outcome for sure.

Another experience with inventing as a solution to design challenges occurred when we were dealing with large American pizza chains expanding into central Europe. Since many of our restaurant chain customers were trying to open restaurants in buildings that were decades and even hundreds of years old, exhaust venting of ovens proved to be very difficult due to ceiling heights, multiple floors to run ductwork through, and prohibitive expense. I asked myself: Why can't the ventilation hood be built into the equipment? So I devised a concept for incorporating a conveyor pizza oven's ventilation into the oven itself and a method to quickly disconnect the oven and vent for moving and cleaning. It was a worthy invention that allowed for easier and less expensive installation. The concept led to many millions of dollars in oven sales due to its unique solution to the ventilation problem that competitors could not duplicate because of the patents awarded.

To achieve success as an inventor, you simply need to recognize challenges like those in the stories above and use applied creative thought to discover a valuable solution. If you do this, you can achieve the level of success and financial reward that you choose and repeat the process over and over again. At one point, I decided to develop a unique steam-cooking device that eliminated the age-old problems associated with steam, namely corrosion of heating elements, slow and ineffective cook times, and excessive service and repairs. It took 30 months of development, but we were pretty proud of the results.

The product's inventive quality was revealed to me in a flash of insight while I was taking a break from development and engaging in totally unrelated activities. I share this story in the pages ahead and it represents one of the magic pieces of the invention creation process: answers to your most perplexing challenges appear when you least expect them and in the most unlikely places. Some call this luck, but with applied techniques, you will learn how to stimulate this phenomenon over and over again to achieve your "aha" moments when you are ready to receive them.

I tell you all this so you know that the advice in this book comes from my direct experience. I believe in its power and the results it can give you. I have over 25 inventions today with a few more in the works. Some have been sold, and some pay me monthly royalties and will for years to come. Some are building a business value as well as paying royalties, creating a future business sale value. I will discuss each approach to monetizing your creative work in Part Seven, "Commercialization."

I decided to write this definitive guide to the invention process to fill the void in literature on this topic.

Invention, I feel, is a unique trade with rules and principles that can be put into practice when they are known. I believe all of us can be inventors to the extent we want to execute the processes that I teach in this book. Doing so can turn you into a lifetime inventor; if you choose, it can guide you to create inventions that provide a lifetime income so you can enjoy sitting back and receiving royalty checks while on the beach or playing golf.

This is a process I follow and have had success following. It is also the process that has been employed for many hundreds of years by thousands of inventors and entrepreneurs and creators of art, music, literature, dance, recipes, and everything else that requires the application of mental process and creativity, but to my knowledge it has not, before now, been documented as a step-by-step process intended to guide any aspiring inventor to success.

My intent with this book is to teach you the process, tools, and techniques to become as successful an inventor as you desire to be. I will also take you through the creation of one of my inventions to illustrate some of the steps in the invention process. I provide exercises and techniques to help you improve certain inventive traits and skills. My purpose is to show you that the process you are about to learn comes from my experiences and learning, not from theory. What follows has served me well, and continues to do so. I hope it provides you with a sense of what you can accomplish by learning and executing the process of inventing.

Any one of us with normal talents and determination can become an inventor. This doesn't mean it's easy, but if you apply what you learn from this book, you can become a serial inventor like those profiled in the pages ahead.

I wish you great success and would love to hear of your experiences and share in your story. Please contact me through my website, https://inventingpathways.com, or email mcolburn.inventingpathways@gmail.com.

## THE KERNEL OF INVENTION

**Even though I had created inventions in the course of my career, I had little idea of the process that generated unique creative possibilities until I studied dozens of inventors and their invention process. My education as an inventor came from studying everything I could find on historic and modern-day inventors. What were their methods, their processes? How did they think? What made their processes work? How did they take their inventions on to success, if they did? I have provided inventor case-study profiles throughout this book with highlights on what we can learn from each. I hope you will find them useful and entertaining.**

# MENTAL PREPARATION

• CHAPTER 1 •

# The Opportunity for Inventors

> You see things; and you say "Why?" But I dream things that never were; and I say "Why not?"
>
> –George Bernard Shaw, *Back to Methuselah*

I **BEGAN SEARCHING FOR** the secrets to the inventive process because I wanted to learn how invention, and the innovation it sparked, played a role in forming and growing our economy today.

As I started writing about the history of inventing, I was at a loss on how to sum up its vast impact on humankind from the beginning of time. I had been seeking a meaningful opening, one that would capture the importance inventing has played in forming our country and culture, and more importantly, one that provided guidance on what the future holds for those who are pursuing inventing today. The answer was given to me when I took a short vacation to Northeast Florida. I found myself in the magical land of explorers and pirates with names like Ponce de León, Sir Francis Drake, Robert Searle, and Edward Teach (better known as Blackbeard). The visit brought back memories about adventures with boyhood friends and our nailed-together wooden swords storming the side of a three-masted galley intent on treasure. As a child, I was always fascinated by pirates, even wondering if it might be a viable occupation when I grew up. My mother thought otherwise.

In an effort to learn more about the adventures on the land and water I was visiting, I sought out the local independent bookstore. I was once again in search of my kind of treasure: knowledge of the things around me and ideas, inspiration, or guidance for my current project, writing this book.

After perusing the bookstore's pirate collection, I picked up a beautiful reproduction of the original *Treasure Island* by Robert Louis Stevenson complete with full-color replicas of the original drawings by N. C. Wyeth. The book was intended for my granddaughter (after I reread it myself, of course). As I headed for the cash register another book cover caught my attention; I picked it up just to look at it. The book seemed to fall open randomly to page 16. It's at times like this, when I am deeply involved in a project, that I am reminded of a line from *The Alchemist* by Paulo Coelho: "When you want something, all the universe conspires in helping you achieve it."

Page 16 was titled "Inventions through Time." The book title is *If . . . : A Mind-Bending New Way of Looking at Big Ideas and Numbers*, written by David J. Smith and illustrated by Steve Adams.

I had found my treasure. On page 16, Smith asks his reader to conceive of the total time that humans have been inventing as a measuring tape that is 36 inches long, which begins with human's first invention, fire (about 790,000 years ago). The text goes on to detail several major breakthroughs in human development. The wheel is invented around the 35¾-inch mark. The last bit of information is what jumped out at me. Smith writes that all inventions of the past 2,000 years are represented by the last tenth of an inch of the entire tape measure. This includes the number zero, paper, plastic, all electronics, space technology, etc. Pages 18 and 19 spell out the inventions of the last 1,000 years using a 12-inch ruler. At the zero end of the ruler, we find gunpowder invented around the year 1000, and in the last inch and a half, we have the electric lightbulb, the airplane, radio, all the way up to the computer, internet, and smartphones.

Invention has led our country's economic and technological growth over hundreds of years, taking us from one distinct economic period to another. It has defined the leading characteristics of each period's development, economic growth, and employment. However, the speed of invention and innovation is increasing and is more concentrated than ever before. As David Smith pointed out with his illustrated history of invention, the pace of inventing increased as time progressed, with all the inventions of the last 2,000 years coming in the last one-tenth of an inch of a 36-inch measure.

This makes sense because as populations increased and life became more complex the opportunities to invent increased as well. Every new invention invites a new invention to enhance, improve, or replace it. I contend that there are countless opportunities to apply inventive process in the actions and encounters you make in your life and the number is growing daily.

The economic era our economy evolved through and continues to evolve in is the large playing field for inventing. Every day hundreds of problems that deal with your occupation, your commute, cooking dinner, cleaning, sanitizing, gardening, golfing, or what have you are being addressed by inventors applying a process to come up with a new and better widget or method.

A brief look at the stages of invention in our history hopefully will provide you with inspiration to look at what is happening today and ways to address new needs with your creative endeavors. We'll jump into the first step of the invention creation process in the next chapter.

The inventions created during our country's agricultural era first improved and increased the output of new crops to feed the growing population. More crops had to be harvested faster and by fewer people, inviting invention of new tools, the tractor, the combine, barbwire, and thousands of other related items. Transportation of crops and livestock, and later tobacco, sugar, linen, and finished goods, had to be improved to address the needs of a spreading population over an expanding land base. This led to canals and water travel, leading to improved means of water transport such as Fulton's steamboat service, which quickly led to continued boat improvements wherever river passage was needed. Canal and river transport was soon supplemented by trains as the transcontinental railway initiated the great era of industrialization. Iron, steel, and lumber needed to be processed, inviting new and better methods. Thousands of inventions contributed to the train and railroad operations themselves. The advent of electrical systems, the telegraph, the telephone, the sewing machine, the alternating current motor, and other great inventions of the golden era of inventing all invited more and better inventions.

For over 100 years, the industrial machine dominated our economy and grew more and more sophisticated with each new invention that changed or improved or replaced some function of an industrial process.

From the first mechanical "computer" in the World War II era to the information age, the pace of invention skyrocketed. We have at our fingertips access to more knowledge than any of us imagined even 20 years ago. We cannot count the number of things we can do digitally (except by a computer). Artificial intelligence (AI) is now the buzzword of computer development; scientists are inventing computers that learn and make decisions, and some admit they can build them, but they don't know how they work (according to Will Knight in the *MIT Technology Review*). What opportunities lie within the pieces of today's digital world? And what of healthcare, space travel, supersonic underground transport, environmental protection? What do these big-growth areas need, and who will provide the answers?

In 2005, Daniel H. Pink, in his book *A Whole New Mind*, argued that we had moved into a new era where conceptual thinking was becoming the force behind economic growth and development. This movement was dominated by creating in ways that digital machines cannot. Pink championed the movement into the conceptual era, where creativity and inventiveness, big-picture audacious imagining, replaced the linear and logical thinking of the computer and information era. As AI grows more prominent in our lives, I believe that we will understand, to a greater extent, how the powers of the human brain applied toward conceptual and creative development will always be critical to our growth and prosperity as humans and as nations.

As each new era is born, the previous one lives on in a decreasing role as its successor grows. The information age is still growing and providing fertile ground for new and improved inventions, while the conceptual age has developed and continues to grow using the tools provided by the information era. I contend that the conceptual age has now spawned the initiation of the artificial intelligence era. One era cannot exist without the benefits of the prior, so as self-driving cars, robots that think, personal electronic assistants that intelligently converse with us, and self-contained cities on distant planets evolve, they are dependent on the continued development of artificial intelligence, and also fueled by the conceptual era's expansive thinking and the information era's logical and linear development. Your opportunity to fill a creative void may reside in the pieces of our economy that need big thinking or it may lie in your backyard through a better gardening tool, a better dog harness, a weed treatment tool, or a barbeque cleaner.

It's up to you to act if you want to be an inventor. There are countless opportunities to apply an inventive process and realize the potential of creating a new and better something. As history shows us, opportunities are everywhere. Success only requires execution.

You will learn the process of inventing beginning in the next chapter. You need to provide the topic you will address as your inventive area. Choose it carefully, as you will spend a great deal of time and money to create a meaningful invention. Ensure that you are passionate about your choice and are willing to make the sacrifices needed to be successful. Make sure the challenge is universal enough to provide a lucrative market for your solution so you are compensated for your time and efforts.

## THE KERNEL OF INVENTION

### • Stephen Key (1956-) •

**Stephen Key started his inventive career selling his handmade goods at art shows and state fairs. He taught himself design and started freelancing, eventually landing a full-time job at Worlds of Wonder, a 1980s-era toy company, working with very successful product lines. But he couldn't help feeling that he could do better than the submissions he was reviewing. Key describes founding his own invention and licensing company specializing in toys. He has over 12 patents on one invention**

*continued*

alone, his Spinformation rotating label product. He began inventing this product after reading a newspaper article that detailed how labels are never sufficient to fit all the required information. This set him on a quest for a simple solution; he developed a spinning label that revealed more information as it turned. It has been applied to various products from medicine bottle labels to drinking cups with animated characters. His numerous products have been sold in stores like Walmart, 7-Eleven, and Disney stores and theme parks worldwide. He has won over 15 international awards for his products in several different industries. Key is the author of *One Simple Idea* and cofounder of inventRight, a coaching business for inventors. He now has a wealth of information for marketing and selling your new invention available through inventRight.

SOURCE: *One Simple Idea* by Stephen Key.

• CHAPTER 2 •

# The Mind of an Inventor

**STEP 1:** Adapt a mental process and techniques used by inventors.

## TRAINING YOUR MIND TO THINK LIKE AN INVENTOR

The first thing you need to do to become an inventor is check some of your natural ways of thinking and, if necessary, apply techniques to enhance your creative output.

This chapter encourages you to take on the thought processes that inventors use and to adopt habits that will enhance your inventive success.

Training your mind to think like an inventor every day in all situations will give you all the ideas and solutions you need to make inventing natural. The more you hone your thought process toward inventive thinking, the more successful your creative efforts will be. Of course no two inventors' minds are alike, far from it. But there are shared traits that inventors possess that are important parts of the inventive mind at work. Once you recognize that these traits are an important part of your work as an inventor, you can sharpen them to get the results you desire.

The chapters ahead will help you apply the techniques of invention and guide you toward nurturing a fine-tuned, inventive mind.

## ATTITUDE OF CONFIDENCE

Your transition begins with an attitude of confidence. You already believe that if you apply yourself you can become the inventor you want to be. If you didn't believe this you wouldn't be reading this book. It is important to foster this attitude at every opportunity and apply it to your daily work.

If you don't believe in yourself it's likely you won't put in the effort necessary to accomplish true inventing. Believing in yourself is a habit. One good exercise to reinforce your belief in your abilities is to set goals. Targets allow you to measure your progress, and you get better at what you measure. Break big goals into small tasks or steps and encourage yourself to accomplish each step. Reinforce your belief and congratulate yourself when each small step is accomplished.

We all possess talent to invent something or many things, large or small, simple or complex. The process begins with knowing that you can invent and then applying the process steps you are about to learn.

It's been argued that it takes 10,000 hours to master a craft (others say this is hogwash), but when assessing what it is going to take to become proficient at inventing, just know that you will get better with every effort and every step you take. You may succeed with your first try, but to become very good at being an inventor it could take an investment of several years and multiple efforts. I had a business and several patents by my 10,000-hour mark, but I was so much better for every hour I worked on my skills and invested the time. This is not a process for those looking for a shortcut. Inventing is a process of dedication and practice. With commitment you will succeed and build your confidence, so let's get started.

• • •

## OPEN-MINDEDNESS

One of the most important attributes an inventor needs is open-mindedness. Without it the process will fall apart. Inventing is the process of exploring ideas and possibilities, recognizing and accepting the unexpected. The willingness to accept change, new ideas, and unexpected insights is paramount to an inventor's success. I have seen competent engineers and designers fail to successfully invent because they had been taught a particular way of doing things and were unable to accept a counterintuitive solution. Contrarily, an open, inventive mind plays with ideas, looks for nonobvious solutions, and tries to make what is considered impossible possible. Taking different approaches to accepted practices reveals unknowns, and unknowns are what inventors seek.

An inventor needs to have:

- A mind receptive to new ideas or information
- An acceptance that things can be different than they seem
- A willingness to explore and consider different ideas even when they conflict with the common knowledge on a subject

When you think you are right, a good practice is to consider that you may be wrong or that there might be a better right answer. This will always keep you receptive to new discoveries.

Being locked into preconceived notions of right answers or solutions kills creativity. Open-mindedness allows you to see new possibilities, to consider all possibilities, and to recognize directions that may provide unexpected results you'd have otherwise missed. If you have a tendency toward being a bit closed-minded, work on it a little at a time. Remind yourself to consider all possibilities before ruling anything out. Challenge yourself to suspend judgment and to not be critical of new thoughts. Just follow them and see what happens.

NutraSweet artificial sweetener was created from an accident, where an open mind caused the inventor to realize that his mistake had created an opportunity. In 1965, Dr. James Schlatter was working on developing an anti-ulcer drug for the drug company G. D. Searle & Company.

Schlatter spilled a flask of chemicals he had been working on. He righted his experiment and went about his work. Later he licked his finger to pick up a piece of paper and experienced an extremely sweet taste, which he then connected to the substance in the beaker. He tested and confirmed that he had inadvertently created a new artificial sweetener 200 times sweeter than sugar without the bitterness of saccharin. A person with a closed mind would not have made the discovery that generated many millions of dollars in commercial value.

## THE KERNEL OF INVENTION

### • Lori Greiner (1969-) •

**Lori Greiner created a unique box that allowed for earring organization. She patented this box in 1998 and produced a sample, borrowing the money to do so. The product was picked up by J. C. Penney before one holiday sales season. About 18 months later, the earring product reportedly "made her rich." She has helped launch more than 400 products and holds 120 US and international patents. She is a well-known inventor and entrepreneur now best known as a cast member on the reality TV show *Shark Tank*. She has been referred to as "The Queen of QVC." She hosts a program on QVC entitled *Clever & Unique Creations Show* and founded a company in Chicago called *For Your Ease Only* for product development and marketing. Greiner used her initial success in one product that made life a little more organized to found a career as a prolific inventor and innovator and become a world-recognized celebrity.**

SOURCES: David K. Williams's article in *Forbes*; Lisa Bertagnoli's article in *Crain's Chicago Business*; and Ami Kassar's article in the *New York Times*.

Try to recognize whenever your thinking puts up a barrier or boundary to an idea. Practice eliminating any boundaries. There are no limitations to ideas. Purposely try to create ideas that are not obvious and that do not seem practical. Imagine fanciful ideas for solving your inventive problems. An exercise we did many times as a group in order to put the collective brain into an open-minded creation mode was to have everyone list *all* the things you cannot do with a paper clip (or some variation of this challenge). When the momentum slowed we pushed to add five more things and to be as crazy as possible. After sharing some of the "can't dos," we would pick one, or one for each subgroup of people, and spend the next five minutes creating a solution to make the "can't do" into a "here's how to do it" solution. It's fun! It usually gets silly, but all minds are open to create uncommon solutions.

## CURIOSITY AND OBSERVATION

> You can observe a lot by watching.
>
> –Yogi Berra

> A few observations and much reasoning lead to error; many observations and a little reasoning to truth.
>
> –Alexis Carrel

### Curiosity

According to author and motivational speaker Michael J. Gelb, in his book *How to Think Like Leonardo da Vinci*, "curiosity," or in Italian *curiosita*, was a very valuable technique in Leonardo da Vinci's thinking process. It is the same with most inventors' minds as well. *Curiosita* carries a much greater meaning than what we normally attribute to our use of the word "curiosity." It exemplifies continued learning; it even has a teaching method named for it (Curiosita Teaching) whose principle is to integrate creative thinking into all teaching and learning. Tomasz Arciszewski, in his book *Inventive Engineering: Knowledge and Skills for Creative Engineers*, paraphrases Gelb by stating that "*curiosita* is seeking the truth or an infinitely curious and open attitude to life and nature resulting in a never-ending learning process." For our purposes, if you adapt a never-ending learning process with a curious and open mind to your inventive interests you will be well on your way to finding the solutions that will be your inventions.

We are all born with the gift of curiosity; it is critical to our learning as infants and toddlers. We tend to suppress a good portion of this trait as our growth and education cause us to use other talents and skills to learn, but our curious ability never leaves us—it simply lies dormant. Curiosity can be nourished and brought back to the forefront of your mind with a little effort and practice. One way to start is by making curiosity a part of your daily activities. Challenge yourself with practice and exercises to become more curious. It will serve your inventive goals well to cultivate your curiosity and make it a habit. Try the exercises below to stimulate your latent curiosity traits.

The very best way to stimulate your mind to be more curious is to adopt the practice of asking questions, especially *what*, *when*, *where*, *who*, and *why* questions. As adults we have a tendency to focus on solutions. You may accept what you hear or see as an answer or the truth, but ask questions anyway. When you have an answer to your initial question, ask a question about that answer. Keep the strings of questions going. You will get better and better at formulating questions and the deeper you go, the greater the level of understanding and eventual discovery. Try starting with the broadest question you can formulate on a particular subject and then narrow each question in the series, or try just the opposite: start with a very narrow question and expand with each subsequent question. Try a writing exercise on a topic, creating five questions expanding the subject or narrowing the subject. Writing will help the process become more instinctual after some practice.

One useful habit is keeping a notebook. In my notebook, I jot down questions throughout my day, questions on just about everything. Not all of them get addressed and some get addressed much later, but just the practice of formulating questions about things and writing them down stimulates my curiosity and improves my skill of asking questions. An inventor's mind is constantly asking questions about the things it sees. Curiosity serves several of the invention step processes we will discuss: insight, hypothesizing, and deduction are each enhanced by a curious nature. Later in the text, we will look at questions for the purpose of idea generation and problem-solving. The goal for you here is to push your brain to be more curious about the things that will aid your inventive efforts. The benefit of honed curiosity is that it aids you in asking better questions of yourself and others. Asking better questions will generate a level of learning that will create more and better questions, adding to your depth of understanding and knowledge on the subject of your curiosity.

Experiment with creating an expanding question list or a narrowing question list of each of the five examples below. This will stimulate your questioning skills, which is key to improving your curiosity.

1. Are racehorses athletes like human competitors?
2. Has life ever existed on other planets or moons?
3. What is a "soul"?
4. Why did the chicken cross the road?
5. Is time real?

I'll try a set of expanding questions; you fill in the answers.

Topic: If a tree falls in the woods and no one is there to hear it, does it make noise?

Q: Is noise just sound?

Q: What constitutes sound? What makes it?

Q: If we were there to hear, how would we hear the noise? Why is what we would hear different if we're not there?

Q: Does vibrating or pulsating air constitute sound or noise?

Q: If animals or birds hear it, but no humans, is it then noise?

Try it! It's just fun.

## Observation

Curiosity is the strong desire to know something, to learn all you can about your subject. It goes hand in hand with observation as a means by which inventors discover the unknown. As you seek more information through being curious, you also enhance your observation skills. You seek to observe whatever will teach you more about the subject of your curiosity.

To be more observant is to be more mindful of what you see. Seeing a dog is not observing, but seeing a dog with several black spots on his brown hide, a slight limp and one runny eye, a coat that is unkempt and would be wet and slimy to touch (further suspecting his odor is rank), leading you to surmise a dip in the nearby swamp . . . this is observing. Develop the practice of asking yourself questions about what you observe; this helps you observe better and can stimulate your curiosity to learn more. (Why did the dog go into the swamp when he could have walked around? Is he sick? Does he have a collar on?)

At its best, observation involves all your senses, not just seeing but hearing, smelling, tasting, and touching where applicable (I wouldn't lick the dog). Make a deliberate effort to apply your senses as you observe something and your skills will be enhanced. Ask yourself sense-based questions about your observations involving feel, smell, and sound to gather more information.

When your state of observation is fully engaged with your senses, you can achieve a new level of awareness that will lead you to greater depths of knowledge on your subject.

Obviously you won't achieve this enhanced level of observation on your first try and you don't need to on every observation. It's only necessary on those observations that are relevant to your goals. Better observation skills means being in a greater state of mindfulness, of being in the moment and focusing on your subject from all possible angles. You will be rewarded with more complete and better inventive concepts as you perfect this skill.

As with open-mindedness and curiosity, observation is a habit you can train your mind to enact. Your natural ability to observe will return and evolve as you proceed to invent. My question notebook comes in handy to make (and remember) observations often supplemented with a photo on my phone.

One story about Nikola Tesla demonstrates the inventive powers of observation and curiosity. Tesla's biographer, W. Bernard Carlson, credits Tesla with being the "inventor of the electrical age." Carlson relates a story that Tesla told of an evening at his family home when he was a youngster. Tesla was petting his favorite cat, Macak. It was a dry winter evening and Tesla thought he saw a miracle when Macak's back turned to a sheet of light and his hand produced a shower of loud sparks. Tesla's curiosity led him to learn about this phenomenon, quizzing his father, who equated the event to the lightning you see in a storm. This set Tesla's mind wondering about this phenomenon called electricity. Later that evening as darkness fell, Tesla observed something like a halo around the cat that seemed to be related to the light and sparks of earlier. Tesla's curiosity and what he called his "childish imagination" about his observed electrical event led to a lifetime of inventive achievement in the field of electricity.

He set about learning everything he could about electricity and spent his entire inventive future harnessing and applying the characteristics of electricity in new inventions. His patents include the foundation of alternating current systems of distribution and electrical motors and generators, with around 300 total patents, all electrical in nature.

Sir Arthur Conan Doyle understood the principals of invention and endowed Sherlock Holmes with many inventors' traits for his detective's use in solving mysteries. One of Sherlock Holmes's greatest attributes was his power of observation, from which he could form hypotheses and deduce the details of many of his challenges. But Sherlock also understood that solving his mysteries was a process, taken step by step, and that hypothesizing and deducing a potential solution to the crime were useless until he deeply analyzed everything he'd observed about it.

As an inventor, one must first learn how to properly observe. In "A Scandal in Bohemia," Sherlock teaches Dr. Watson what truly observing means. Dr. Watson is baffled by Holmes's process of deduction based on observation and states, "And yet I believe that my eyes are as good as yours." Holmes replies, "Quite so," lighting a cigarette and throwing himself down into an armchair. "You see, but you do not observe. The distinction is clear. For example, you have frequently seen the steps which lead up from the hall to this room."

"Frequently."

"How often?"

"Well, some hundreds of times."

"Then how many are there?"

"How many? I don't know."

"Quite so! You have not observed, and yet you have seen. That is just my point. Now, I know that there are seventeen steps, because I have both seen and observed."

You will find reason to reflect on this exchange and to engage your power to truly observe in every step of your invention process. Through detailed observation you will gain many insights and opportunities that will aid in true invention.

Improving your powers of observation and honing a technique whereby you become curious about things you observe can provide you with endless insights, inspiration, and ideas. Practice being more mindful wherever you go: the dentist, grocery store, health club, airport, or anywhere else. What's that tool going to do in my mouth? Why are they dumping snow into a large dumpster on the tarmac? (They were transporting to a snow-melting machine area.) My grocery store removed all the fresh juices; why? Observe everything you see and ask yourself questions about what interests you—then ask more questions if something *really* interests you.

Years ago I was visiting a large client with close to 1,000 employees. I arrived with the employee I was working with at the beginning of the morning shift. The parking lot was huge, but I noticed almost everyone entered through the same set of doors. We entered along with the throngs of people with their bags of donuts, cups of coffee, and breakfast sandwiches. We took the elevator to my host's office. He offered me coffee from the office four-pot machine (one pot with burned coffee coating the bottom). The counter was a mess with wet napkins, spilled cream and sugar, and a wastebasket with coffee grounds and empty cups. I declined. I asked if every group of offices had its own coffee setup. We visited the central kitchen dining room for lunch, and I observed a full-service coffee setup along with breakfast items untouched throughout the morning. My observations led me to talk to some employees, and I took a little survey to support an idea that these observations had led to. The result was we helped the food service operator design a cart, with a selection of quality coffees, bagels, donuts, and packaged foods along with some wrapped breakfast items from the central kitchen. The cart was placed inside the entrance from the parking lot. Employees stopped shopping on the way to work, saving them time. They bought quality products just before heading to their work spaces and most offices abandoned their messy coffee setups. The cart, with one employee, generated over $1,000,000 in revenue for the company the first year.

Watch other people and how they do certain things. Before long, your power of observation will become automatic and you will feel more deeply connected with everything around you.

Here is a good practice exercise for improving observation; it can work anywhere, but an airport is particularly good. Pick a person and study them (undetected). See how many details you can observe and jot them down; watch actions and describe them, note how much more you see than you normally would.

Trained observers go deeper and deeper into what they have observed, as Sherlock Holmes explains to Watson in "The Boscombe Valley Mystery": "You know my method. It is founded upon the observation of trifles." In mystery after mystery, Sherlock observed the minutest details overlooked by Watson and inspectors from Scotland Yard to piece together his theories, create deductions, and hypothesize solutions.

In closing this section, I want to emphasize that working on your inventive mind traits is a lifelong endeavor, even when you are starting at an advanced age. The more effort you put into it, the more fine-tuned your skills will become, and the better inventor you will become.

To summarize, it's extremely important to approach your inventive efforts with an attitude of confidence—"I can do this." Keep an open mind to all things related to your efforts; you never know where the answers reside. Practice the techniques of being curious, ask questions and more questions, and train your senses to take in layers of details in what you observe. Train your mind to think like an inventor (Step 1).

### THE KERNEL OF INVENTION

#### • Joy Mangano (1956-) •

Joy Mangano began inventing as a teenager working at an animal hospital. Seeing that many dogs they treated were struck by automobiles, mostly at night because they were hard to see, she created a fluorescent flea collar to keep pets safe. She researched materials, sketched designs, and showed the results to her boss, who liked it and showed it around to veterinarians he knew, who all approved of the solution. The collar helped pets rid themselves of fleas and also helped prevent accidents by making the animals visible to traffic. As a teenager, Joy didn't know about protecting her product and didn't know how to get it to market, and she became distracted, so the invention sat idle. A very similar commercial product was released by Hartz Mountain Corporation about a year after her solution was developed. Joy learned a valuable lesson while she was still a teenager: it's not enough to create a worthy product. You have to protect it and get it to market.

After graduating from Pace University, she worked as a waitress and an airline reservations manager while raising her three children as a divorced mother. She returned to inventing after she became frustrated with ordinary floor mops. She invented the Miracle Mop, a self-wringing mop head, in 1990. It was made from a continuous loop of cotton that could be easily wrung out without getting the user's hands wet. With what money she had and investments from family and friends, she made a prototype and manufactured 100 units. She began selling the mops at trade shows and at local Long Island stores. She then sold 1,000 units on consignment to QVC. The mop sold modestly at first, until Joy was allowed to go on the air and sell it herself: she sold 18,000 mops in less than a half hour. Ten years later, the Miracle Mop was selling at a rate of $10 million per year.

Mangano now holds more than 100 patents for her inventions. She is the founder and president of Ingenious Designs LLC and appears regularly on the US shopping channel HSN, where she is considered to be HSN's most successful purveyor. In 2017, she released a book called *Inventing Joy*, published by Simon & Schuster, and *Joy* is the title of a 2015 movie, which was loosely based on her life and for which Jennifer Lawrence was nominated for the Academy Award for Best Actress.

SOURCES: "Cinderella Without a Prince" by Allison McNearney; *Joy* by Fergus Mason; Susan Konig's article in the *New York Times*; Trang Ho's article in *Investor's Daily Business*; and *Inventing Joy* by Joy Mangano.

• CHAPTER 3 •

# Establishing Inventive Directions

**STEP 2:** Find the problem you will solve with an invention.

**SETTING SAIL WITHOUT** a destination will leave you lost at sea. In this second step in the invention process, you examine your passions, your frustrations, or your great hopes until you find a worthy objective for your applied inventing efforts. As you will read, not all problems need to be solved, so choose wisely.

Picture the following:

*The city: London.*

*The location: a small third-story flat in the late 1800s.*

*It is a dark and stormy night.*

*Rain is beating against the windowpanes.*

*A strong wind is howling through the city streets.*

*Suddenly, across the flat a candle flickers through the darkness and a tall, thin man emerges from a bedroom.*

*He walks slowly across the room.*

*The candle flame reflects in his intense dark eyes.*

*He gently taps the shoulder of a man asleep.*

*He says sharply, "Come, Watson. Come, the game is afoot."*

If that scene evoked fond memories, you are likely well acquainted with the magic and mystique of the Sherlock Holmes legend.

As I noted earlier, Sir Arthur Conan Doyle understood and used the same creation processes that a good inventor uses when he created his stories. He created a direction for his detective in the form of a crime or mystery and then empowered his detective with the same techniques, the same steps, methods, and processes used by inventors, to solve the mysteries that are chronicled in the four novels and 56 short stories that make up the Holmes collection. The only difference is that Holmes started with a problem to solve; you have to find your own. I first encountered Holmes as an analogy to creation-related processes when I was conducting my own study of inventive process for our business in a paper called "Sherlock Holmes and the Educational Process" by Richard L Kellogg. My mission was to find out what steps and processes successful inventors used to invent.

## THE NEED FOR DEFINING A PROBLEM

Before inventing you must first define a problem you intend to solve. Establishing this inventive direction will help you know where you are going and what you hope to achieve; it will help you measure your progress as you proceed toward a solution.

It's no different than an author beginning a new book or an artist starting a new painting: you make little progress until you have a direction.

Where does direction come from? Where do you begin? Sherlock Holmes had his problems presented to him in the form of a recent murder or an investigation requested by those who sought out the world's first consulting detective. The mystery gave him the starting direction he needed to apply his processes to solve the crime. Holmes had murders or missing people or a caper to solve. His problem statement was easy: "Who killed the red-haired lady?" He was at an advantage over us. His problem was already defined by the actions of some criminal. We usually need to identify problems from scratch.

Let's spend a little time on the nature of problems, their purpose, and where to find them.

Doyle's novels start with a mystery, a lot of unknowns. If the novel were to open with the solution, what would be the purpose of reading it? The fun and the reward come from figuring it out. It is the same with inventing: you have to start with a good problem to have a good invention. If you want to get really good at inventing, get really good at finding good problems to solve. Your problems will contain a lot of unknowns as well and by investigating these unknowns you will follow a path to invention.

Problems invite solutions and provide the formula for someone to create that solution. Problems create new possibilities. All invention begins with defining a problem or a set of problems, and then examining all aspects of those problems, defining the unknowns before you begin any creative work. Consider problems as opportunities; start by focusing on problems that are clear and have a recognizable need. These problems are more likely candidates for market success.

Once found, your problem becomes your focus; it gives you direction, it is the reason you are pursuing this inventive undertaking. Your problem gives you a beginning, a place to start. Creating its solution is your defined goal.

## WHERE TO FIND PROBLEMS

Designate an amount of time daily to focus on finding a suitable problem. Focus on finding your problem in all your daily encounters and activities. Keep your mind alert and open; rule out nothing. Your skills of observation and curiosity are tools in your quest to find the problem that is yours to solve. Look for problems in everything you do, everywhere you go, in everything you read; they are all there waiting to be found and solved by the curious observer.

Think about James Dyson, who thought the vacuum cleaner was antiquated; he made it his problem to invent a superior machine to replace all existing vacuum cleaner designs. Later he did the same thing with hand dryers.

Joy Mangano decided the rag mop was messy and hard to use. In her mind, it needed to be replaced with an improved solution. She made it her goal to do just that. She later reinvented the clothes hanger to huge success. Most of her contacts wondered why the clothes hanger had to be improved; she showed them why with a better solution. Both inventors are successful and wealthy today because of the problems they found to fix and the success of their solution.

During the heyday of using personal cameras, the public became frustrated with having to send film and sometimes the camera with the film to a lab and wait two weeks to get their pictures back. This led Edwin H. Land to invent instant photography and, a year later in 1948, the Polaroid camera. Land changed the process of photography forever. There are millions of problems worth solving that are waiting for an inventor to find them.

It doesn't matter where your problem comes from as long as it has sufficient meaning to keep you motivated throughout the work you will have to do to create a worthwhile inventive solution. It's a good idea to spend some time studying the potential for your solution once you feel you have a worthy problem. Check the competitive products, if any. Who will buy your solution, individuals or a company? Who are the likely prospects to buy or license your invention? What is their history with new products or systems? Talk to some of the marketing people that deal with related products: "What if there was a product that . . . ? Would you be interested?" Even if money isn't a principal motivator for you, having a ready market for your solution is an important consideration if you will be depending on your ideas to pay for your inventive activities—or if you hope for your inventions to succeed with a particular audience.

As indicated at the start of this section, very often your problem can be found in the activities that you know best, what you work with every day. It can be your profession, a hobby, housework, or something you encounter taking care of the children or commuting from one place to another. The problem can come from something you hate doing (removing the grass between the bricks on the walk is one of mine). The problem can come from an area you become greatly interested in from an observation or from the influence of some event in your life. Your problem can come from a higher purpose such as eliminating hunger or providing safe drinking water to Third World countries. In the activities you do, the things you observe, the things you are passionate about, the things you become really frustrated with, or the things you read or talk to your friends about, there are numerous opportunities to find worthy problems, be they large or small.

Many inventions are not solutions to original problems and many famous inventors were not the definers of the problem they solved. Likewise your inventive challenge may be established in the work of others, only waiting for your inventive addition. You will find that there are many existing problems in need of an inventive solution. If others have worked on the problem you have chosen, a wealth of information may be available for your use, and your solution might just enhance what already exists.

The Wright brothers were not the first to work on a heavier-than-air flying machine; many had tried and were trying when the Wrights created the defining solution of wing warping to control the flight. They took the work of others, defined what didn't work, and added their inventive component. The lightbulb had been around for decades before Edison created a longer-lasting bulb and an improved method of electrical distribution. Edison also took the work of Alexander Graham Bell and invented several improvements to the performance and appeal of the telephone. If you look for problems that others are working on, you may find your inventive direction refined or defined for you. By studying the body of work related to this approach, you learn what hasn't worked and can apply inventive practices to come up with your own unique solution.

As a twelve-year-old boy, Thomas Edison worked on the railroad selling newspapers and other sundries to passengers. Three years of traveling the rails between his hometown of Port Huron, Michigan, and Detroit and back allowed Edison to make friends of both travelers and men in the telegraph offices of the various stations along the way. The men enjoyed encounters with the young man and laughed at the troubles that seemed to spring from his various attempts to keep his active mind engaged. Use of the telegraph was growing rapidly along with the spread of railroads and the initiation of an army corps of telegraph operators. Edison begged operators to let him practice his coding and recording skills. He practiced with a homemade setup and even constructed a telegraph line between caves in his backyard to a friend's house a mile away. Finally, a family friend (and telegraph operator) took on Edison at age 16 as an apprentice and brought him along enough to get a job as a part-time operator. Edison was never great as an operator, but he learned the equipment and the principles behind the technology and carried this with him throughout his career. He held jobs as an operator in several cities, being fired from most of the positions but advancing his knowledge along the way.

His first embodiment of a new device was due to his inability to interpret Morse code fast enough to improve his standing as an operator. His solution was to take two antiquated pieces of equipment that embossed the dashes and dots of transmissions on paper that he linked together so one received the signals and repeated them through a clockwork mechanism that reproduced the code at a slower speed so Edison could interpret the message. He solved his problem with a clever solution and was eventually fired from that post for his effort.

Telegraph was limited in the distance it could travel at this time. Messages with destinations more than 200 miles apart had to be sent to intermediate stations, interpreted by an operator, and resent to the next station until it arrived at its destination. Edison wondered why the Morse recorder he used for his speed alteration couldn't be rigged up with a transmitter that would automatically repeat the code and send it onto the next station, eliminating the added labor and occasional error of reentering code. After some failed attempts, he succeeded in developing the repeating system and demonstrated it to his station master, who promptly reprimanded him for wasting his time on useless activities instead of attending to his job. He also became very unpopular with telegraph operators for trying to put them out of a job. He had found a worthy problem and solved it, but he did not have an interested market. He left for yet another post as a telegraph operator in another city.

In 1867, Edison quit the life of a traveling telegraph operator. He briefly returned to Port Huron but found his family deteriorating; his sister had died, his brother was aimless, and his mother was showing signs of mental illness. Edison needed to escape this environment as soon as possible. He put out inquiries for positions, networking with his old cronies. Eventually this resulted in landing a position with Western Union in Boston. Inspired by a secondhand set of volumes on electrical research by the English scientist Michael Faraday, Edison decided he needed to accomplish more with his life. To his roommate Milt Adams he is reported to have said, "I am now twenty-one. I may live to be fifty. Can I get as much done as Faraday did? I have so much to do and life is so short, I am going to hustle." He began his career as an inventor.

In 1868, he read about a problem the Washington, DC, city council and New York state legislature were having with tracking and recording votes. Edison merged his knowledge of transmitting electrical impulses via telegraph and the process of printing telegraphs to invent a vote recorder. He was issued US Patent 90,646 and he developed full working models of his invention. He defined his problem solution (speed and simplify voting by electrical transmission and mechanical recording means). He created a workable solution. Unfortunately, what he didn't do first was study the problem adequately to determine if there was a real need. When his vote recorder was reviewed by a committee of Congress, the chairman stated, "If there is any invention on earth that we don't want down here, this is it." He explained that the slow pace allowed for further debate and for member filibustering, which was considered useful in convincing some members to change their mind on votes. The committee felt this more desirable than speed. The invention failed and was never sold or used. Dejected, Edison vowed from his previous invention failures to never undertake an invention again without a known commercial need. In 1869, he publicly declared he was to become a full-time inventor. He moved to New York and opened a business to manufacture telegraph equipment. In Boston, he had already made significant progress on producing a duplex telegraph, a device being sought by Western Union at the time.

The second step in the invention creation process is to find your problem, but it is then advisable to investigate your problem thoroughly before investing your time and energies in solving it. You will want to ensure the problem is worthy of what you have to invest.

Identifying problems related to your knowledge base and experience has another often-overlooked aspect. Yes, your problem gives you a direction, but your knowledge may lead you to solving a different problem altogether. The process of defining a worthy problem and attacking it will lead you toward a meaningful invention even if you end up solving a problem you didn't know you were working on. You're inventing, not solving equations, so if the process leads you in a new direction, you might just invent a more meaningful solution.

In 1775, James Watt, a Scottish mechanical instrument maker; John Newcomen, a blacksmith; and Thomas Savery, a military engineer, had problems with the reliability of water pumps. They decided to create a better pump design (their inventive problem). Watt was fascinated by steam raising the lid off a pot of boiling water. Studying how pumps worked, the three men experimented and observed the effects of water pressure, vaporization, and condensation. The results of their work fueled the industrial revolution and formed the basis of transportation systems and turbines for electricity, among hundreds of other uses. They created a steam engine, and they were working on water pump problems.

Alexander Graham Bell was schooled early in the science of sound, as both his grandfather and father were. They were recognized as experts in the field of voice and elocution. Bell was to follow in their footsteps. But he also became fascinated by the telegraph and set up experiments to convey signals with electrical current.

But soon he had an opportunity to renew his career in language arts by moving to Boston, where he established himself. Even with a busy workload as a prominent teacher of the deaf, Bell continued to think about telegraph technology and soon set up a space to continue experimenting late into the evening on many nights.

During the late 1860s and the early 1870s, Western Union was seeking technology to send multiple telegraph messages in the same or two directions on one telegraph wire at the same time and made it known that the inventor of such a solution would be well rewarded. From sound experiments he had read about, Bell felt that sounds could create electrical signals conveying multiple telegraph messages at one time that then could be reproduced on the receiving end. He set his sights on inventing a harmonic telegraph to solve the multiple message problems. Western Union had defined his invention problem for him. His training in sound drove him toward an audible solution. Bell didn't start out to invent the telephone. His original problem statement was to create a harmonic method for sending and receiving several written messages at the same time over telegraph lines. The work he did to solve the telegraph problem helped create key concepts for his telephone invented in 1876, which eventually replaced a lot of the need for telegraph.

Meanwhile, Thomas Edison was also on the case, applying his knowledge of the telegraph to help solve Western Union's problem. He set about creating a multiple messages machine for Western Union (the Quadruplex in 1874). One attribute of his experiment recorded messages by inscribing the dots and dashes on foil with a needle. Through his work on this machine, he came up with breakthrough discoveries that led to his invention of the phonograph in 1874. Like Bell, Edison solved one problem by working on another.

The Edison and Bell examples bring out other aspects about problem-solving with inventing. First, the problem you tackle may come from a challenge someone else is trying to solve, and second, most problems have been tackled before in some fashion. The problem might not be new at all. Your approach to solving your problem may be new, but groundwork and concepts that have come before often can serve as the starting point for your inventive work. Bell and Edison used existing telegraph technology as the beginning of their problem-solving. The Wright brothers didn't come up with the problem of human flight; people had been working on it for hundreds of years. Edison didn't come up with the concept of a lightbulb: there were dozens of lightbulb projects before his. His work was to take the problems that existed with lightbulbs and create a better solution. Edison looked for problems with inventions that were already created to do a lot of his work. Bell's telephone didn't really work all that well. Edison invented a carbon-button transmitter (microphone), which made using a telephone much more practical.

Challenging problems are spelled out all around you. Many are described in journals and magazines and in newspapers. Look for problems to solve or technology that can be applied in ways different from what you read. Look for inspiration from what others are working on and the directions these advancements are taking. When you tune your mind to be alert to identifying a problem in what you observe, read, and experience in daily life, then the process of identifying invention-worthy problems will become automatic. The harder part will then be to choose wisely when you endeavor to solve a problem.

**TIPS, TECHNIQUES, AND TASKS FOR FINDING A PROBLEM WORTH SOLVING**

1. Assign yourself time daily to look for and think about what your problem might be. Your problem may pop into your mind with a flash of definiteness to it, or you may find a number of possibilities to ponder. Either way, the process will sooner or later deliver the problem that will be your project's starting point.
2. Get a permanently bound notebook with numbered pages (a lab book or similar) and dedicate it to your inventive efforts. Track your steps, questions, observations, and progress. Mostly capture every idea you have about your problem. Sketch and doodle about your problem. Note obstacles and complications you run into.
3. Maintain a list of questions related to your problem. Document all the questions you can think of to begin your quest for greater knowledge of your problem.
4. If you haven't arrived at your problem yet, assign yourself a task to observe everything about your day for two weeks. Make notes in your notebook on what you observe. What needs to be improved? Why? What frustrates you? Why? Before going to sleep during the two-week period, tell yourself that you will identify your problem by the end of this period.
5. See the movie *Joy*; observe when the problem was discovered and when it became a purpose, a direction for Joy Mangano to create a new and useful invention.
6. Read *Popular Science*, *Mechanics Illustrated*, *MIT Technology Review*, *Science News*, *Scientific American*, *Discover*, and other similar publications. Very often problems being addressed in articles can stimulate a direction for your efforts.

## THE KERNEL OF INVENTION

### • Artur Fischer (1919-2016) •

In the introduction, I referenced a simple device that cost less than a penny to manufacture and which now produces and sells over 14 million units daily around the world. From Artur Fischer we learn that simple solutions to everyday problems can be very popular and lasting and that some of the most useful and profitable inventions don't need to be complex. By his history we also learn that continued application of the invention creation process can build an impressive portfolio of inventions.

Artur Fischer was a lone inventor and a natural problem-solver. Born in Germany, he left school at 13 to apprentice with a locksmith. After serving in World War II, he returned to his homeland and started a business making lighters and loom switches out of military scrap. A decade later, he created his best-selling invention: the expanding screw anchor wall plug that allows screws to be fastened into materials that normally wouldn't support heavier objects. This is the product referenced above; however, this invention was later challenged by a Swiss patent claiming an earlier invention date and the challenge was upheld. A lesson here is that multiple inventors can be working on the same problem at the same time; therefore, protecting your inventive ideas quickly is important. Fischer decided to take his design and apply it in new ways: he used the expanding plug idea and created a plug for fixing bone fractures. Fischer went on to create hundreds of inventions, among them the synchronized flash for cameras. He invented a cup holder with a retractable lid and a Lego-like construction toy. At final count, he had over 1,100 patents (more than Thomas Edi-

*continued*

son's 1,093). The final lesson from Fischer is that you can continue to apply your invention creation process over and over again to generate as many inventions as you like.

SOURCES: Fischer's obituary in the *New York Times* by William Grimes and various internet references.

• CHAPTER 4 •

# Forming Your Problem Definition

## (Creating Definiteness of Purpose)

**STEP 3:** Prepare a written statement describing your inventive problem, the need for a solution, and your commitment to delivering it.

The formulation of a problem is often more essential than its solution. —Albert Einstein

All problems have solutions, but solutions don't exist without defining a problem. —Unknown

**ALBERT EINSTEIN WAS** reported to have said that if he had one hour to save the world, he would spend fifty-five minutes defining the problem and five minutes finding the solution.[1]

While it is tempting to jump right into creating a solution once you've discovered a problem, doing so is not likely to provide you with the best outcome. Once you are sure you have the problem you intend to solve, it is critical that you spend time thinking through every detail of the problem without trying to solve it.

1 There is no source validating that Einstein actually said this and there are multiple variations on the quote. The point is that problem definition is key to solving your problem.

Einstein understood that by adequately defining a problem you set in motion the creative process necessary to devise the solution needed. By adequately addressing the problem the solution would appear.

## FORMULATING YOUR PROBLEM STATEMENT

Your next two actions are to document what you know about your problem and then summarize it in a statement that encompasses your commitment to a solution. These steps are important to your success because they focus and direct your thought process toward a solution. These steps could make the difference between success and failure on your invention. Spend some time writing about your problem. Try to fill a couple of notebook pages with everything you can about your problem and the reasons it needs to be solved. When you are done, work with your results: combine statements that seem like they should be together, eliminate what seems to have no purpose.

Next, write a clear and concise description of the problem you will solve; this will become your problem (purpose) statement for the project. Spend the time you need at this task until you are thoroughly satisfied with your statement. Some points to consider:

- Begin with the "why" definition of your chosen problem. Describe what the problem is. Why is it a problem? For whom is it a problem? What are the reasons this problem exists? What circumstances led you to choose this problem? What negative effects does your problem create? What causes the problem?
- How can a solution benefit others when it is created? This is critical not only in justifying your problem choice but also to finding your solution's potential in the marketplace. Spend a little time (not a lot at this point) defining what the market is and why.
- Describe the results your solution must accomplish. What are the critical things a solution must deliver?
- Describe in as much detail as you can your vision for your solution's final form. (Is it a machine, service, software, electronics,

substance, method, etc.?) You do not have the end result yet (you don't want to have the end result yet), but describe what it will be, how it will perform or appear (even if there is some repetition with the previous activity).

- Give yourself responsibility for coming up with this inventive solution for your problem/purpose statement. Write a statement of your individual goal; formalize this as a foregone conclusion. Be very definite in your statement. Declare your determination to deliver a solution to this problem.

Following are two examples of problem statements for projects of mine, one a commercial product, one a consumer product. These are just examples; your problem statement is personal to you, so make it your own.

### PROJECT 1: New Ventilation Need

One of the most versatile new pieces of commercial cooking equipment is the combination convection air and steam oven. These ovens are in high demand but present obstacles for a buyer. Most kitchens that are already built (over half the potential market) do not have exhaust ventilation equipment that can accommodate these new ovens. Adding a new ventilation system to accommodate one or more of these ovens, venting to the exterior of buildings, when even possible, often costs several tens of thousands of dollars.

When these ovens are installed without a ventilation system, which is usually against local codes, a great deal of heat, smoke, grease, and moisture from wet condensing steam infiltrates the facility, which is uncomfortable and unhealthy.

I will undertake a project to invent a self-contained ventilation system that can be oven mounted and accommodate multiple brands of ovens. This solution will not only treat the oven's vented hot air and steam but capture and treat the emissions from opening doors. The solution will have to filter out grease and particulates but will also have to treat smoke, cool the air, and chill the steam to an acceptable temperature for discharge into a drain (under 180°F). The treated, cooled dryer air will be vented to the space.

This is a worthy project with a motivated (waiting) market. I know I can develop a unique solution based on our prior work on ventilation and with steam; the uniqueness will come from capturing and cooling emissions through the use of chambers in the "vent" and unique sensing and cooling components.

This work will be completed and tested in a looks like/acts like prototype by the next NAFEM [a trade show] in 18 months.

This project resulted in the award of US Patent 9,567,082: Apparatus for converting hot air and steam emissions into cooler air and condensate.

### PROJECT 2: A Personal Travel Aid

Frequent travelers have a clothing problem. Wrinkled clothes can present a less than desirable image. Furthermore clothes after a few days of travel can get musty or less than fresh smelling. Ironing is a nuisance and if the clothes aren't fresh can seal in odors and soiled spots. Hanging clothes in the shower frees up the ironing time but is wasteful (and in one case expensive—a friend fell asleep with the shower on and it peeled the wallpaper off the wall; she spent hours trying to repaper the bathroom using the Gideons Bible as a tool). Handheld travel steamers are heavy, prone to leaking, and do not last very long due to corrosion of the steam chamber. Plus they take just as much time as ironing.

I will invent a lightweight, easy-to-pack clothing steamer that attaches to a garment bag. The steam will generate in a corrosion-free manner and be easily cleaned. The bag can hang on the shower rail or in the closet and the traveler can relax with a glass of wine. The unit will have to shut itself off when it runs out of water. The uniqueness will exist in the steam generation method, the combination of bag and generator, and in the shutoff means. Adequate steam will remove wrinkles in most clothing and freshen the fabrics at the same time. An odor neutralizer might be added

(Febreze like). I will complete this project with working prototypes before the next visit of [customer] in February.

This project resulted in the awarding of US Patent 8,464,562: Garment Steamer.

The wording of your problem/purpose statement is essential: you will refer to it hundreds of times, and you will have it memorized. Repeating this statement reinforces your understanding of what you are trying to accomplish and helps focus your creative juices both consciously and subconsciously.

I generally set this first draft to the side for a day or two and then come back to it. I clean it up a bit, tighten it, making sure that I agree with everything I wrote and that it is as clear as possible (not just to me, but I try to write it in a way that would be clear to anyone reading it). I then commit it to a separate piece of paper and tape a copy where I can read it periodically, at least daily. This has now become my statement of purpose for this project, the goal. It is definite and provides all the background I currently have on this particular problem. It declares that I will be the one to solve this problem.

## DEFINITENESS OF PURPOSE

Andrew Carnegie is probably the first to define "definiteness of purpose" as a necessity in successful endeavors. My definition of "definiteness of purpose" is to know exactly where you are going and how you intend to get there, then write it down, committing yourself 100 percent to the process of achieving this purpose. You don't know all the answers, but by being committed to the purpose, you will complete the journey.

Your problem statement captures your definiteness of purpose, which is the point where you begin moving toward a solution to this problem. It is the kickoff that takes you into the real effort of invention.

I'm repeating myself, but it is very important to recognize that by defining your problem and focusing on it, you give yourself the direction you need to accomplish your task. Your thought process will do the work, but you must be very definite in the problem description.

Denis E. Waitley is an American motivational speaker, writer, and consultant. He is the best-selling author of the audio series *The Psychology of Winning* and books such as *Seeds of Greatness* and *The Winner's Edge*. I have kept a quote of his on my office wall for years. It reminds me of the reasons for the work you just did on your problem/purpose statement.

His message is that the mind needs "specific instructions and directions" to process and deliver the results you seek. Waitley states, "The reason most people never reach their goals is that they don't define them and learn about them." He further states that you need to seriously consider them as "believable or achievable."

When I read Waitley's advice, I am constantly reminded to reinforce the direction I assign to my mind's activities and my current purpose of inventing or creating.

There is a deep purpose to writing your problem definition. Doing so prompts your conscious brain to create precise instructions that your creative or subconscious brain will understand as a direction. The more you reinforce this direction consciously, the more your creative brain will apply its skills on delivering a solution. Your problem/purpose statement provides your conscious and subconscious mind with specific instruction and direction. We will delve more into this mental process in upcoming chapters.

Definiteness of purpose is about knowing what you want and conveying it to your creative mind. It is also about giving up on any thoughts of not achieving your purpose. It is when you decide, once and for all, to eliminate all obstacles on your way to achieving a valuable solution to your stated purpose. When you eliminate all negative thoughts about not accomplishing your goal, you give your subconscious permission to move toward a solution. When your creative brain knows you are serious and positive about this effort and nothing will stand in your way to achieve it, obstacles will be removed and your mind will work its magic.

• • •

## SUPPORT YOUR PURPOSE

Definiteness of purpose can have magical properties, but before we move on, one word of caution: once you know your direction, define it in clear terms, and assign it to your creative mind, you assume the responsibility of supporting your goal with your actions. You are the support system for your thought process. You have given life to a quest to create a unique solution to your selected problem; now you must feed it, nourish it, become the action figure of the tasks at hand and the sage that guides your thought process to accomplish what you want to achieve. In other words, you have to do the work and provide the tools to make it happen. You can't sit back and wait for magic.

## DEFINING MY WATER HEATER PROBLEM

I will use one of my irritant problems as a simple example of creating a problem/purpose statement. This story actually includes a couple of our inventive efforts modified for its use here. The development will continue to unfold in the upcoming chapters.

As an exercise you may want to read the next few pages and practice narrowing them down to a functional problem statement.

- Every time I need hot water in my bathroom, two flights up from the basement water heater, I wait minutes with the water running before the first warm water arrives. I hate wasting water and time. Wasting water will eventually be a bigger problem than wasting energy and will impact our lives in greater ways, including the ability to feed the people of our planet. However, I am not passionate enough to stop washing my hands or taking a shower with hot water. This is a problem for all homeowners who rely on a single water-heating source to supply hot water to all faucets in their home. If we assume an average of 2.2 gallons per minute of water flow, and three minutes' wait time, I waste 6.6 gallons of water every time I turn on the hot water faucet after 20 minutes of nonuse. I usually turn on the water and wait for it to heat up four times a day—a waste of 26.4 gallons of unused water daily (and a waste of 12 minutes of time). Multiply this by hundreds of thousands or millions of households and there is a need for a solution that eliminates this waste, provided other resources such as energy aren't wasted in use of the solution. I believe this is an opportunity to create a solution that will save us from wasting millions of gallons of water annually and create a convenience of time-saving to all users.

- The reason this waste happens is that the water lines between water heaters and hot water faucets are pressurized and filled with water between uses. Once flow stops, this hot water in the pipe cools off as the time lags between uses, wasting the energy it took to heat it. This water has to be drained through the faucet before hot water can reach the sink.
- My solution will benefit others by removing an irritant that I am sure is not just mine and will result in a savings of a user's time and a reduction in wasted water and heating energy. It will help save water to help save the planet.
- My solution must deliver hot water, at 120°F or hotter temperature, immediately when a hot water faucet is turned on, without wasting water, without the use of excessive energy, and without a costly installation process. I do not want something that keeps water hot between uses as this would waste energy.
- I envision a point-of-use in-flow water booster heater, small and lightweight that can be added to the final run of hot water piping (perhaps with flexible piping) and plugged into a convenient outlet or wired to a convenient junction box. This heater will heat flowing water as it passes a point and must be able to produce up to a 70-degree rise in temperature. This heater must shut down automatically when water from the hot water heater arrives at the point of the heater at the desired temperature. Since resistance heaters take time to heat and first have to heat their element and sheathing before they heat the water, I intend to find a way to directly heat the water without a resistance heater (the inventive challenge).

- I am not a scientist or electrical engineer, so I will need to consult with others to create a viable solution or sufficiently study specific technology to create a working model. [Note: often inventive solutions come from those who are not directly involved or experts in the area to be addressed with invention. This is sometimes beneficial to coming up with a unique solution. Information and techniques can be found and studied and experts consulted for almost all areas of development. (As a side note, I first hired a university researcher to find all the articles he could on different ways to heat liquids for any use.)]
- I strongly believe that this is a worthy problem to solve and has sufficient commercial value. I will create a new and useful, nonobvious instantaneous point-of-use water booster heater that is easy to install, is inexpensive and does not waste water, and uses a minimum of energy. This is my focus and I will find the solutions to every obstacle that presents itself during the development.

Once you reach the point where your problem has been defined and you have established a clear direction for your inventing efforts, you have achieved definiteness of purpose. Your mind starts to work in a different way; the more focused you become on your single direction, the more insights and opportunities make themselves known to you as you proceed with your work.

Some inventors prefer to write a simple summary to their problem statement, which is easier to reference more frequently when committed to an index card or piece of paper you carry with you. For the water heater problem I would use:

> Create a point-of-use water booster heater that heats flowing water instantaneously without wasting energy, creating up to a 70°F rise in temperature. Make it small, inexpensive, and easy to install.

Sometimes a simple flow diagram or sketch with notes can be a part of your problem statement to provide visual input to your creative effort. The following is an example:

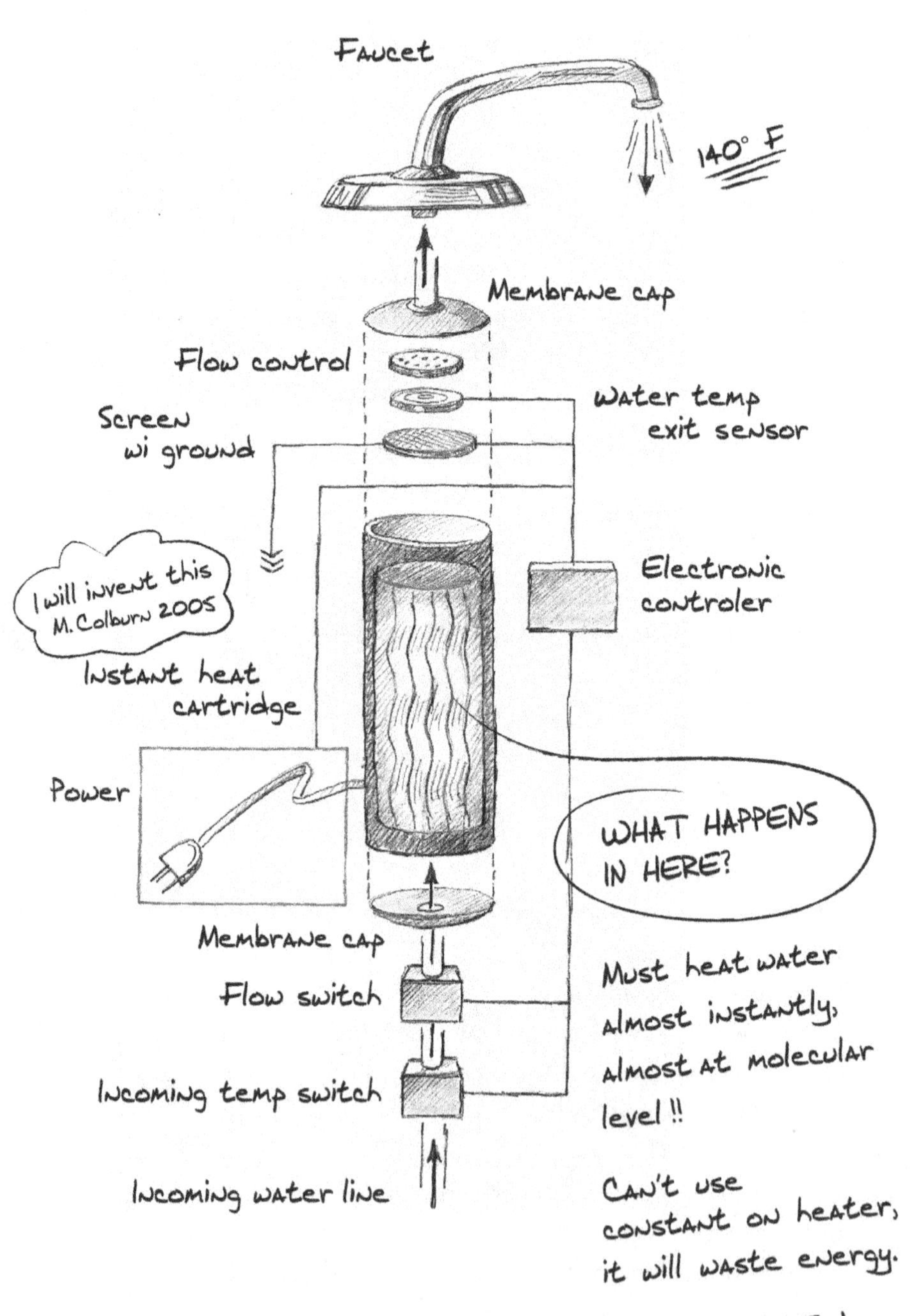
Faucet
140° F
Membrane cap
Flow control
Water temp
exit sensor
Screen
wi ground
I will invent this
M. Colburn 2005
Electronic
controler
Instant heat
cartridge
Power
WHAT HAPPENS
IN HERE?
Membrane cap
Must heat water
almost instantly,
almost at molecular
level !!
Flow switch
Incoming temp switch
Incoming water line
Can't use
constant on heater,
it will waste energy.
THIS IS THE INVENTIVE CHALLENGE !

When you complete this work on a problem statement, you have set a goal of inventing a solution to your chosen problem, thereby planting a seed for your mind to work on. It's your mystery to solve; the more you think about it, the more you will observe and that will aid your efforts. Having a defined goal is the most important part of inventing; everything else is execution. You will devote time, energy, and money to achieving this goal; you will live with it every day, so ensure that you have chosen well and it is a goal worthy of your efforts.

**HINTS ON DEFINING YOUR INVENTIVE PROBLEM**

1. This is such an important step! Don't be in too much of a hurry to complete your problem statement and move on. You not only need to believe this is the problem you wish to solve, but you must also understand as much as you can about the existing nature of the problem and take time to study, observe, and think about your problem before writing the problem statement.
2. As mentioned earlier in the chapter, don't worry about not knowing enough about the field or science of your chosen problem. You are the conductor, or the quarterback if you wish. You can assemble sources for the knowledge needed.
3. Create several drafts before committing to your final problem statement. Make sure you have worded everything in a way that truly supports your thinking. Think about the creation of important works like the Declaration of Independence or the Bill of Rights; they took many drafts, but the words all resonate with us today because each one was carefully chosen and placed.
4. Even though I am emphasizing the need to focus on your purpose and commit to it, your definition and solution statement may change as you research the problem and define your efforts. The steps are intertwined and you may go back and forth between defining your purpose statement and research, but knowing what your objective is in defining your purpose will aid your research.

5. Sometimes the problem you identify isn't the root problem, or what needs to be solved. In my water booster example, getting hot water to my bathroom sink faster (what I first defined as my problem) isn't the problem to be solved. In creating my statement and diagramming what was needed to solve the hot water problem, I eventually identified that the problem to solve was instantaneously heating water molecules in flow.

When you're through with your observations and information gathering by applying a curious approach to understanding what you have identified as a problem worthy of invention and by committing yourself to creating a solution and defining your goal through your problem statement (establishing definiteness of purpose), you have progressed through the first three steps of the invention creation process. Your mind is functioning like an inventor's mind and getting better at it every day as you have defined a problem, are asking more questions about your problem, and are feeding your curiosity on what its eventual solution will be. You have created a definite problem statement, and concurrently with these steps, you have accomplished the most important aspect of inventing: an internal commitment to solve this problem. This has set your success mechanisms to work behind the scenes, and your creative talents are at work absorbing and observing everything that could possibly aid your efforts by providing clues to your eventual success.

You must now do the work of feeding your thought process with as much knowledge pertaining to your problem as you can. Later we will discuss how your mental process is working and how to use and enhance these processes, but first—to the research.

## THE KERNEL OF INVENTION

### • Leo H. Baekeland (1863-1944) •

Leo H. Baekeland used a firm foundation in chemistry to adapt knowledge from one field and apply it in new and inventive ways to another field. He also chose a problem that others were working on and explored new directions of solving this problem to create an inventive solution.

Baekeland became fascinated with photography at an early age. He engaged himself with mixing chemicals for developing pictures and for printing. He followed this passion into university and by 21 had earned a summa cum laude doctorate in chemistry from Ghent University in Belgium. He had difficulty concentrating on his assistant professorship of chemistry and would spend a good deal of his time delving into the local manufacture of photographic plates and emulsions. He was drawn into commerce to promote a fledgling company that would market his first invention, an improved plate for photos that was simpler to use but tricky to manufacture. He eventually gave up the effort for an associate professorship position.

Baekeland traveled to America at age 26 on a scholarship. Newly married and with his bride by his side, he never went back to Belgium. He quickly became involved with a camera club in New York City and made valuable contacts among the group.

Baekeland arrived in the city just as George Eastman introduced his first Kodak camera using film. Eastman was struggling to get control of supplies of photographic paper to support his camera's success. Baekeland followed the news on Eastman and chose to solve the photographic paper problem.

Baekeland fully absorbed himself in perfecting a new photographic paper. This caused difficulty with his family when his wife returned to Belgium for the birth of their first child and Baekeland stayed to work on his paper. He was struggling

*continued*

with little income, working at a photography company as a consultant, exploring various inventive ideas, and incurring increased debt. He was working to exhaustion until he became seriously ill.

While ill, Baekeland made an important decision that would affect his inventive future and contributes a valuable lesson to those of us pursuing invention as a career. He realized that, instead of "keeping too many irons in the fire, he should concentrate all his thoughts and attention on one single thing that would provide the best chance for the quickest possible result."

His health eventually returned and he focused all his efforts on experimenting with silver chloride emulsions on photographic paper, testing several hundred variations. This led to an improvement in photographic paper that allowed photographs and enlargements to be developed by artificial light instead of daylight. He named the paper Velox and formed a partnership establishing a company to market his invention. Velox caught on with the amateur photography crowd and became competition for Kodak's paper, called Solio.

Eastman summoned Baekeland to Rochester, New York, to discuss a deal. On the train ride to Rochester, Baekeland struggled with what to request for the rights to his invention.

Upon entering, Eastman declared to Baekeland that he would purchase the "damn" paper for one million dollars, "and not a penny more." There are references to Baekeland having been willing to sell for $100,000. A lesson here is to know what the market value of your invention is, as much as possible, before entering into negotiations. You might not be as lucky as Baekeland.

The deal ran into complications, since Leo did not have full ownership rights to his invention because of his earlier partnership, but he did have full rights to the process. The ownership rights involved the Belgium cartel that had made supply deals with Eastman. Eventually a three-way deal was cut providing Baekeland with a share of $750,000, making him a wealthy man. (The value of $750,000 in 1899 is equivalent to over $22 million in 2017.)

Following the transaction, Baekeland and his family lived a life of luxury, which he did not condone; he sought a simpler life. He had a small chemical lab on the grounds of his home, but he had no purpose, no project of importance. Through his sale agreement, he was prohibited from working in the photographic field for 20 years. The sale of Velox made him rich but removed his drive and purpose.

After a couple of years working as a consulting chemist on projects, he set out to find a new promising area where his expertise in chemical engineering could be turned into new inventions. Learning from his former experiences, he focused on finding one problem that could provide the quickest results.

Synthesis, or creating new compounds by bringing together their constituent parts, was a relatively new science. In some circles, the process was considered alchemy and was even opposed by church doctrine.

Around this time, scientists in Europe and America were desperately seeking a substitute for natural shellac, originally used as a finish for wood products. A shellac substitute had become even more essential as an insulator to support the growth of electrical components. The problem with shellac was that it took 15,000 beetles six months to produce a pound of shellac and they died as a result.

Baekeland took up the challenge in 1902 with assistant Nathaniel Thurlow. Picking two of the simplest compounds already tested, phenol and formaldehyde, they carefully repeated all the experiments by others that had failed in order to ensure that he had experienced all the errors already conducted. This is a great example of the research you put in to fully understand a problem direction before venturing into creating a solution. Like all those before, their experiments ended with an unmanageable solid that would not react to any solvent.

Baekeland studied the roles of the variables encountered by the compound reactions in various experiments to connect the

*continued*

problems with the results. This was a breakthrough approach to experimenting: preceding chemists had studied results by chemical analysis or simply moved onto another solvent and hoped for different results.

Based on their work, Thurlow followed the original objective and took a feasible shellac substitute to market called Novalac. There are products today that duplicate the process and use of this product (not to be confused with the baby formula of the same name). Baekeland was curious about the material they produced. Could anything else useful be created from the substance?

Baekeland observed and analyzed the work they had done, looking for improvement and opportunity. He felt the bubbling when heating the chemicals was a problem, which could be controlled by pumping air into the heating vessel during processing. Baekeland experimented with adding pressure to increase the temperature. He felt the reaction was being conducted at too low a temperature and raised the temperature to twice the boiling point of water. The next observation he made was that he could control the reaction by adding a dilute acid to the mixture, which produced a clear thick liquid. If he added alkaline substances, the final product he produced was a hard, clear insoluble solid, resistant to acids and heat. These discoveries allowed him to select the hardness of the product before manufacturing by controlling the acid. These are all examples of experimentation and observation leading to greater discovery based on hypothesizing results based on assumptions.

He spent two more years perfecting his process, and the result was the creation of the first truly synthetic, moldable, machinable product, resistant to heat and solvents and inexpensive to produce. He became the inventor of plastics—Bakelite, as he named his product. It went on to become one of the most successful products ever and is used in tens of thousands of applications.

Baekeland succeeded where others failed through a combination of inventive process skills. He acquired a body of knowledge on photographic processes and techniques related to chemicals, he became educated in chemicals, and when challenged to solve a problem where other chemists were failing, he became curious of the results. He studied the processes, applying a test to all variables in the process similar to his photographic process experiments, and applied techniques not considered standard by the chemical community. He formed hypotheses, experimented, and keenly observed the results. Because of his detailed process and keen observation, he is considered the "father of the plastics industry."

SOURCES: Harold Evans's book *They Made America; George Eastman: A Biography* by Elizabeth Brayer; and various internet references.

• PART •

# RESEARCH

• CHAPTER 5 •

# Acquiring Specialized Knowledge

**STEP 4:** Learn everything you can about your problem.

Chance favors only the prepared mind.

—Louis Pasteur

**YOU HAVE YOUR** purpose; you are now feeding your creative powers with the raw material they will use to deliver your unique solution. The key function of knowledge is action, and knowledge is the fuel that powers invention. Without knowledge, you risk wasting your energy with a poor solution or failure.

Eureka or "aha" moments (bursts of insight) don't just happen out of the blue. They are the result of preparation, a critical step that feeds and nourishes your defined purpose so your creative brain has what it needs to deliver the answers you seek.

You must put meaningful time into gaining specialized knowledge about the problem you have chosen. This is your research step, and it is essential to your success.

The specialized knowledge step of the invention creation process will prepare your mind to recognize possibilities and solutions when they become evident in your work on your chosen problem.

• • •

## GET TO KNOW YOUR PROBLEM

We are all impatient. It is difficult for a fired-up inventive mind with a definite purpose to properly slow down and take the time to research, but it is absolutely necessary for true inventing. You will need to systematically accumulate information related to your problem. The task at hand is to gather, organize, catalog, and understand everything you can find related to your specific problem. Two inventive processes are at play here:

1. To create something truly new, one must first know what exists.
2. An inventor must learn as much as possible from all the existing knowledge in order to give the creative mind the tools it needs to create unique solutions.

By studying the existing body of knowledge on your given problem, you will come to understand the limitations that have previously existed, the obstacles that were overcome, and the outcomes of the solutions that currently exist. It is likely that new possibilities will pop into your consciousness as you gather and organize these facts.

A good exercise is to break your problem down into components or sections and research these separately from the whole problem. For example, my research for water boosters changed from research on water heater systems to heating water, to properties of water, to methods of BTU transfer, and deeper.

Note all possibilities you think of in your notebook; catalog data so you can reference your research as needed. I recommend using a laboratory notebook, such as the ones available from Scientific Notebook Company (https://snco.com). Each page is numbered and you should date each entry. There are also lines for having a third party witness certain notes if they might be inventive (not necessary but sometimes useful). There are spaces to note references on other pages to make it easier to link related information. As a secondary step, write yourself a series of questions related to your research as they pop into your head.

Especially ask "what if" questions, for example, "What if I did this instead of what's done here?" The notes you take will become your cues as you develop your invention.

This bears repeating: it is extremely important to take the time to seriously execute this research step. It is fuel to fire your creativity. Don't just gather material; spend the time to truly understand it. In his book *Juice*, Evan Schwartz credits Jay Walker, founder and chairman of Walker Digital, with saying that employees are not looking closely if they "can't find six sides to a problem." He uses the quote when hiring new inventors and hands them a Rubik's Cube to keep at their desk as a reminder.

The internet is clearly a great resource for information, but don't limit yourself to online research. Visit libraries and talk to research librarians. I quiz college professors, I read textbooks, and I gather all the prior research papers on a subject. I search issued patents and pending patents and read them word for word, sometimes several times. I do the same with foreign patents (Google translation helps), although I rely more on the drawings with foreign patents. This allows me to know how others approached a solution to my problem topic. I study competitive products serving the same or similar problems (or an opposite problem). I sometimes buy and use competitive products and even take products apart to study the components. I look for products that are not competitive but have some similarities in sometimes random ways. For example, when we were creating a new machine for steam cooking, we studied all the cars in the parking lot (our own cars) to look at latching solutions and gasket solutions for sealing the doors against pressure.

Sherlock Holmes swore by his research step in his crime-solving. He kept detailed notebooks of all types of subjects so he could always relate data to references when needed. When presented with a mystery to solve, Holmes felt it was a mistake to establish theories until sufficient investigation of the facts had been accomplished. He felt that premature theorizing causes the investigator to misinterpret the facts in order to fit the theories. It was better to approach each problem with an open mind and let the evidence decide which of the possibilities to pursue. In *The Adventures of the Copper Beeches*, Sherlock exclaims, "Data! Data! Data! . . . I can't make bricks without clay."

This applies to invention research as well as solving mysteries.

Valuable research can also be done by talking to people who have some connection to the problem you are solving. When Norman Brinker was working on fine-tuning his Chili's restaurant concept, he made a habit of walking around the parking lots of competitive restaurants and talking to customers who had just dined, asking if they liked their meals and what changes they would like made or what would improve their dining experience. On the basis of this research, he began to shift the focus of Chili's menu and experience. Through the process he invented a new restaurant concept.

## FINDING RELEVANT INFORMATION

There are thousands of ways to gather information. Get as creative in the fact-finding as you will be in inventing your solution and you will be hugely rewarded. As quoted earlier, Louis Pasteur said, "Chance favors only the prepared mind." Putting meaningful time into your research will prepare your mind for coming up with solutions. Once you spend time studying a good problem, you will be amazed how things jump out at you from all sources providing clues to your eventual solution. When your mind is prepared, useful information and solutions will present themselves to you in many different ways. Be ready to receive this information by keeping an open mind.

Most of the inventing work I have done has resulted in utility patents and, therefore, involves some form of mechanical or electrical solution combined with design and functionality aspects. As you will learn, solutions for your particular problem have usually been created already in some fashion. Prior solutions can be very useful to creating your own unique problem solution.

If your chosen field of problem has a trade show, go to it to learn from those who are involved in the industry. Talk to the salespeople—they love to tell you what's good about their technology and why it's superior to the competition; visit the competition, too, and eventually you will see the gaps you can fill with your inventive solution. Often manufacturers bring engineers and designers to trade shows. These people don't get to talk to as many people as the sales employees, so engage them—you will learn a lot.

The patent search is one of my most valuable tools when tackling a problem. Early in your research process you will want to conduct some patent searches on your own. The reference documents you find related to the patent you are researching (other patents, papers, or documents) are referred to as "prior art." When you find "prior art" associated with a patent it will have "references cited." This is a list of patents or documents referenced by the inventor or examiner that were compared to the patent being examined. This expands your list of references, and sometimes has more value than the base patent you have found. The "prior art" you receive from the patent search will provide insight to what has been done by others over the years related to your problem. This is extremely valuable to your education on your problem and eventually on your solution creation.

Two sources will aid your patent research. If you have a patent number, Google Patents (https://patents.google.com/) is your best source. In most cases, you won't know a patent number to begin with, so visit https://www.uspto.gov/patents. There you will find a tutorial on searching and will have access to most patents issued and patents pending since 1995. (Patents issued between 1790 and 1995 are only searchable by issue date, patent number, and current US classification.) With some keywords related to your subject, you will be presented with a list of patents (or applications) that semi-relate to your topic. It takes a little time, but the next step is to eliminate what you expect won't be of use. There are two ways to do this: first, narrow the search with additional keywords to supplement your initial list. Second, skim through the titles, looking for words that indicate a relationship with your topic (I print them and mark them up in case I want to go back and choose others). Then one by one pull up the "abstracts" only and read them to see if you can determine their contribution to your effort. Occasionally I pull up the images to help assess its pertinence. Only when I determine that there is valuable information in a particular patent do I print it and put it in a binder.

## ORGANIZE YOUR RESEARCH

Taking the time to organize your research materials will aid your solutions work, improve your focus, and save substantial time when you have to locate a critical piece of research during your development period. You will also find that when your research is organized in an orderly collection it allows your knowledge to grow and compound in a searchable pattern. Your ideas then tend to build on one another, adding more possibilities to your creative efforts.

Again the laboratory notebook is a handy aid here. It allows for an extensive table of contents and each page has an area to reference prior and future pages with relevant related notations. Taking the time to keep these up to date can save you countless hours later when you need to find that critical piece of information. Notations, sketches, clippings, and even doodles can be given names and then entered into the table of contents and cross-referenced by page number.

You will find the deeper you get into your research, the more you learn and the more questions you will have. This is good; the questions are leading you toward a greater understanding of your problem. This result will continue through the entire inventive process.

When you have gathered, organized, and cross-referenced your raw material, you should have lots of data. This material contains the ingredients that will guide you toward your inventive solution. What do you do with it?

## HOLMES ON RESEARCH

Our hero, Holmes, compared a man's brain to an empty attic that could contain only so much furniture. "There comes a time when for every addition of knowledge you forget something that you knew before," he said in *A Study in Scarlet*. It was his way of saying you need organized research you can consult. Holmes kept data from many sources on current and past criminal activities. His apartment at 221B Baker Street was cluttered with boxes of clippings from which, Watson conceded in one story, his associate could quickly furnish information on almost any subject or individual. Holmes pasted clippings into scrapbooks, cross-referenced and indexed them, and wrote notes in the margins. We of course have databases, spreadsheets, scanners, and cloud storage organizing systems, so it should be easier than it was for Holmes, but it still needs to be done.

Organize your data in a way that can be easily studied, easily referenced, and referred to over and over when necessary. You are not going to remember every detail you find, but at some moment in your efforts, your mind will flash to something important that you suddenly remembered from your research and you will want to find it quickly.

Use whatever system works for you, but always keep your notebook, dedicated to this one project, handy for your thoughts and observations, questions, sketches, and ideas. As I mentioned above with the patents I find on patent searches, I create binders and use a sticky flag (the thin type lawyers use) to mark sections with pertinent information. I create a simple table of contents for each binder (priceless). For research papers, I will use a database, either Google Docs or Evernote. I don't recommend relying completely on the digital tools; the handwritten data in your notebook is more usable for singling out just the information that is pertinent from all the larger documents you store in your database.

## STUDY YOUR RESEARCH

As you locate your reference data, study it, take notes in your notebook (again, note where the reference document is kept), write on paper documents, and get to know the details of your raw material. Some will lead you to dozens of other references; pick and choose what will be meaningful to you. Look at each piece of information one at a time and from different angles. Consider each fact you garner as a piece of a jigsaw puzzle and ask yourself questions like: "What characteristics of this fact affect my problem?," "What connection does it have with my problem?," "Where might it fit in a solution?"

## Research on the Water Booster Problem

I studied many trade sources for my water booster project, not only on heaters but heat exchangers, circulation pumps, industrial heating appliances, and heat exchange fluids, and I consulted with a chemist grad student at our local university, paying her for a few hours of her time. I gathered all the material that could be found on any way water could potentially be heated, even if the technology had never been used for water heating. I studied this information and included it in my notebook and database.

I had basic research to do on the specifics of my problem, and I needed to know if it was unusual in any way or if there were many homes with the same problem. I spent time on this topic searching and talking to editors of trade journals and administrators of related associations. You can usually find a list by searching online, but the in-depth information should come from the sources. Examples of sources I used are *Process Heating* (journal), *PM Plumbing and Mechanical* (magazine and online), and the PHCC: Plumbing, Heating, Cooling Contractors Association, and very valuable information came from *Appliance Design Magazine*, including their product forecasts and shipment data, which helped define the market potential.

I needed to know what solutions already existed, which came from patent searches. By entering keywords that I compiled from some of the trade journal work (water heating, booster heaters, heat exchangers, etc.), I researched the patents to see what others had done and how they did it. I expanded the search in some obscure directions, like the melting of metal in factories and electrochemical processing. I researched the market to see if any of these solutions were commercially viable or available. This literally generated thousands of reference documents, which I trimmed down to the most pertinent. I was not yet trying to create a solution, but as I studied each document, ideas started to percolate, so I wrote them as question statements in my notebook, such as "What if I used a heated fluid at the point of use and exchanged its heat to the water? Would it be fast enough (I don't want to keep it heated all the time as that would waste energy)? Is there a way to heat water instantly? Would it be fast enough then?"

## CONSULTING THE EXPERTS

No matter how much time you put into research, there will be gaps. If your problem is complex at all, you will be missing key bits of information that can be supplemented by finding the right resources to assist you. Colleges and universities are great sources for finding someone, student or faculty, who can shortcut your research. You can even work with someone remotely if you don't have a local institution with the expertise you need. Businesses with expertise in a particular field can often offer assistance. Trade associations, retired engineers or professionals, and local associations or clubs that are related to your problem area can also be useful. The difference here is that you often have to pay for some time to gather information from these sources, but often it is an insignificant amount. On one occasion, we needed a computer analysis to project what the air movement results of a particular vent concept would produce. It cost more than an insignificant amount but gave us clues to how our solution would work without building a prototype and cost a fraction of what hiring a professional engineer to do the same work would have cost. We consulted a university professor who was coaching a grad student, and it became a study project for the student who had access to the professor's proprietary computer analysis program. It ended up being a bargain.

Nothing clears up a line of thinking better than stating it out loud to another person who has knowledge of your field of invention and then fielding questions. Speaking out loud forces you to pause, reflect, and think about how you phrase your statements and to be fully mindful of the thoughts contained in your spoken reply. You slow down your thinking and weed out what isn't important. Talking with others also forces you to think differently about the material, thoughts, and premises you have gathered. Hearing the verbal description also communicates clearer messages to your brain.

Few inventors have all the knowledge they need to create complete inventions. This is where developing a series of sources can come in handy. The internet can connect you to contacts that specialize in certain disciplines for one-on-one work and online chat sites can provide insights into specific problems. If you need to hire expertise for research activities (which can often be avoided, but I've had to do it on occasion), posting to a university job board or contacting the intern office of a university or trade school can provide sources. A few words of caution, though: many "experts" know what they know and know that they know it. This is the very antithesis of open-mindedness. This doesn't mean avoid their input. Seek it out, by all means—it's valuable. But you have to decide what input to accept and what information you might attempt to disprove later. Known facts are just that; they are previous discoveries. You are pursuing unknowns and will use known data as your jumping-off point. Development that is truly new will be critiqued as unachievable or impractical before you prove otherwise. Accept critique and use it as a tool to work past the objections.

## FINDING CLUES IN "IT CAN'T BE DONE"

I was told by a leading expert that water couldn't be heated faster than the current technology allows. He explained that a certain number of BTUs had to be transferred from heaters into the water to achieve a certain temperature and the heaters had to heat themselves first to do this. This was from the top engineer of a world-leading company that manufactures appliances for heating water. I didn't disagree with the science, but buried in his statement was the solution challenge that needed to be overcome. Yes, a certain number of BTUs had to be transferred into the water, but if I could eliminate the heaters, skipping this middle step, could I get the water to heat itself? I continued to look for ways to do it differently.

When confronted with closed-minded information, get all you can and then work to disprove those pieces that are important to devising a solution to your problem.

Your research and investigation will have no end because new information will always be required as you discover new twists and turns throughout your process. You can't, however, research forever. When you feel you have a solid basis in your topic, it's time for action, time to move into the creation steps of the invention creation process. You will find that it's a back-and-forth process when you find a new topic that needs research in order to proceed. But to invent you must now apply the work you have done into a creative process.

## THE KERNEL OF INVENTION

### • George Westinghouse Jr. (1846-1914) •

George Westinghouse was one of the great industrialists of the gilded age (the period between the Civil War and World War I). He was known by some for his gentleness and kindness to friends and workers alike. By others, he was known as "Crazy George" and was said to be easy to anger and would throw fits of rage. What is less known is that George Westinghouse built his industrial empire on the back of inventions of his own design and those he acquired from numerous inventors, combining intellectual property and modifying intellectual property for alternate uses to build commanding businesses in several fields.

Westinghouse developed himself into one of the great inventors and engineers of the day, and we can learn a good deal from his techniques.

Westinghouse was constantly observing problems, looking for opportunities to problem-solve and turn the solution into monetary gain. He understood that it was necessary to find problems big enough to justify investing the time and effort into a solution.

George Jr. benefited greatly from working in his father's machine shops and from the interaction with the employees, machinery, and processes that were used to manufacture agricultural equipment and tools, including small steam engines that were growing in popularity at the time. George Jr. was not a good student in school, but he was proficient at math and drawing. By the age of 10, George Jr. could set up machinery and machine parts on his father's equipment. By the time he

*continued*

was 15, George Jr. could design, engineer, and build steam engines on his own. He envisioned improvements to steam engines and undertook to research and study everything he could find on them, even going back to a steam device from the second century BC known as the "Sphere of Aeolus," a hollow ball that would rotate on an axle when steam was forced through opposing hollow tubes. (To see a picture, check online.)

George would continue to work on his steam engine improvements for years, but it was not the steam engine that set his course in industry.

Over the early years, Westinghouse settled into a process of observation, research, design, and invention that is worthy of study. Quentin R. Skrabec Jr., in his book *George Westinghouse: Gentle Genius*, describes how his methodology for design and invention evolved, beginning with detailed research before embarking on his process of inventing. Once he had researched a problem, George would start with freehand sketches combining ideas with notes and questions to arrive at a concept for an inventive solution. Having engineering skills, he would then create dimensioned drawings to build a prototype for testing. He would repeat the process if necessary to arrive at his solution.

Railroads were the boom industry of the 19th century and were responsible for rapid growth of support industries and businesses. Such rapid growth of a technology and its associated businesses is always ripe with opportunity for improvement and invention. When George Jr. left his father's business and struck out on his own, it was the railroads he would observe and study. He knew that inventing for the railroads could lead to major financial success. He looked for a problem to solve and discovered his first opportunity in the constant delays passengers experienced when a train car derailed. A tool existed for rerailing a train car, called a "car replacer," but it often failed due to the weight and pressures placed on it. Westinghouse felt it wasn't designed very well. He sketched solutions in the notebook he always carried with him and eventually created a design that improved the rerailing process, cutting the time from a couple of hours to under a half hour. The common approach to rerailing a car involved workmen pushing and pulling the derailed car over the replacer tool onto the track. Westinghouse devised a piece of rail that would allow the locomotive to pull the derailed car back on track instead of using just muscle power. In addition, knowing the existing replacer designs' failures were from metal fatigue, he researched materials and swapped the wrought iron originally used in replacers with steel to provide greater durability.

From his constant observation of the railroad operations and the success of his car replacer, he next undertook to redesign the track-switching mechanism, which allowed trains to change tracks. These devices were known as "frogs" and longevity was an issue here as well. They failed often, requiring rail lines to replace them.

Westinghouse learned that hundreds of these switches were replaced monthly and the railroads ran up considerable losses due to the inability to move product or people for periods of time. He went to work sketching, modeling, and testing to achieve an improved product. His practice of intensive research led him to explore casting steel to overcome the durability issues of wrought iron and cast iron. He studied everything available on casting methods and entered a period of experimentation leading to one of the earliest steel castings. Both his car replacer and his new frog design would become cast steel products, providing railroads with cost savings and reductions of lost revenue. In patenting his frog, Westinghouse hit on the concept of redundancy, designing so key parts could be reversed when one wore out, giving the railroad customers double use of every purchase. He would carry this concept forward into many of his products throughout his career.

As Westinghouse's railroad supply business grew, he developed relationships that would lead him in directions of greater

*continued*

need. He was always on the lookout for highly profitable opportunities from problem-solving. His first two successes had been improvements to existing products and provided his business with revenue but were not the major product he desired. Over time he set his sights on improving braking systems for trains. He had been playing with the idea for some time as he built his car replacer and frog business.

Westinghouse observed a head-on wreck of two freight trains that caused the passenger train he was traveling on to be delayed for hours. Train cars in those days each had their own brakes and the brakes of each car had to be applied to slow and stop the train. Brakemen would have to travel from car to car applying brakes. Often crashes or deaths occurred in the process.

His mind started creating ideas even though he had not yet begun the serious work of developing a solution. This will happen for you as well as you continue to observe and keep a notebook of observations and ideas.

Westinghouse wrote that the first idea that came to mind, which he afterward found had been in the minds of many others, was to connect the brake levers of each car to a gear to be applied from the locomotive. He did some experimenting and even created some models but realized it was a poor solution. The work, however, stimulated his thought processes that had worked for him in the past. He declared that he would be the one to create a solution to solve the problem with value and benefit to all involved.

In essence, Westinghouse assigned a mission to his subconscious brain to deliver a solution to simultaneously apply power to all the car's wheels at the same time. He became fully resolved to create the unique solution that would make train travel and transport safe through reliable and efficient braking.

Because of his history with steam, his next inventive thought was of using steam for braking, placing a steam cylinder under each car with a pipe connection extended to the locomotive so that the steam would be transmitted to all cylinders by one action from the engineer. After experimentation, this solution was likewise ruled out as problematic because when steam condensed in the lines it caused a loss of pressure and the brakes would fail.

At this time George read a magazine article that described the building of the tunnel in Mount Cenis in Europe, where they substituted compressed air for steam to keep a uniform pressure traveling through thousands of feet of pipe to power the drills and other equipment deep in the mountain. Westinghouse had found his inspiration and the first part of his solution to the train brake.

Westinghouse designed, prototyped, tested, and built the first significant compressed-air device in the United States, which he applied to solve his train-braking system. His design allowed the engineer to apply all brakes to the wheels of all cars simultaneously from the locomotive engine. To apply the brakes, the engineer opened a valve allowing compressed air to travel to each train car's brake cylinder, applying the brake shoes simultaneously. When the brake was released the compressed air was released to the atmosphere and travel continued. This was a major breakthrough in railroad braking, and after successful trials, the Westinghouse Air Brake Company was born.

However, Westinghouse soon realized the solution was not without flaws, which he had to correct in order to convince the majority of railroad companies of the value of investing in the air brake. Primarily if a railcar became uncoupled, the airline was severed, which released the compressed air and the braking would fail. This is when Westinghouse's true epiphany occurred: What if he reversed the process? What if he made the air pressure keep the brake shoes off the wheels? In this way, stopping the train meant decreasing the air pressure, which allowed the brake shoe to descend against the wheel. If a coupling broke, air pressure was lost and the brake was applied

*continued*

automatically. He received multiple patents on his air brake designs and this success laid the foundation for his empire. He was 23 years old.

In his lifetime, George Westinghouse received 361 patents on his work. His understanding of the importance of owning intellectual property to gain competitive advantage and to successfully innovate product drove him to acquire or produce another 3,000 patents within his organizations.

From George Westinghouse we learn:

1. The value of extensive research into your chosen problem.
2. Sketching and drawing are efficient idea generation tools.
3. Modeling and testing solution ideas can help find failures to eliminate, saving time and money, as well as proving successful ideas. These are important steps in inventing.
4. Improving existing products can provide valuable inventions.
5. Observation is a powerful tool to understanding your problem and for finding keys to its solution.
6. Solving big problems for major industries can generate more meaningful returns.
7. Sometimes taking your chosen solution and reworking it or reversing it can generate major breakthroughs to your design.
8. When your subconscious is engaged in finding your solution you often find inspiration and ideas when you least expect them.

SOURCES: Quentin Skrabec Jr.'s book *George Westinghouse: Gentle Genius* and internet references.

• PART •

# CREATIVE THINKING

• CHAPTER 6 •

# The Creative Brain and Cooperative Mind Functioning

**STEP 5:** Assign the tasks of solution to your creative brain.

**STEP 6:** Use mind messaging to communicate with your creative brain.

**YOU ARE NOW** beginning the creative portion of the invention creation process. This is where the magic happens. We will explore the brain's role in invention and learn about how your mind works and aids you in the invention process. We will learn about the two hemispheres of your brain and how they are different. Knowing how they are different and how to apply each to your objectives is where this process will take us. The two hemispheres don't always cooperate. They need to be encouraged to do so. When they do, I call this "cooperative mind functioning," and when used habitually, it becomes a powerful "cooperative mind alliance." To fully utilize your mental functions toward invention, it is important to execute your creation talents at both the conscious and subconscious levels, causing them to work together toward creation. We will detail the practice of creating communications between the two parts of your brain and how to create a left brain/right brain mind alliance where the minds cooperate in their respective functions to deliver on your objectives.

We will detail how to create specific messaging to deliver directly to the creative brain to aid and promote maximum results from subconscious thinking, and in the next chapter, we will provide you with exercises to stimulate inventive solution ideas using cooperative mind functioning.

Picture your brain. It looks a little like a walnut, right? It has two halves that pretty much look the same with a narrow canyon running down the middle. Each half contains part of your mental process. The left side controls the right side of your body and the right side controls the left side of your body. The two halves are connected by millions of nerve fibers. Each side of your brain is usually referred to as a hemisphere.

Within each hemisphere resides a different thought process, one conscious (the left) and one below your consciousness, one you don't directly hear; hence, the use of the name subconscious (the right). I will use this term "subconscious" interchangeably with the creative brain.

## LEFT BRAIN/RIGHT BRAIN CHARACTERISTICS

The left brain is verbal; it is the center of speech and language, it is the seat of logic, and it solves problems and plans actions in an organized way by analysis and reasoning. It works in sequential, orderly, patterned ways. It is your tool for taking action, getting things done, and executing plans. Your left brain wants to talk. It thinks, reasons, plans, solves problems, and therefore feels it knows the answers. This can be good, of course; however, in a creative endeavor such as inventing this is not likely to result in the breakthrough concept or the unique solution without cooperation from the right brain. The more you can establish a cooperative working relationship between your left and right brain the more successful you will become. Your left brain must relinquish the tendency to have all the answers and invite input and answers from the right.

The right brain is visual, nonverbal. It has spatial awareness and intuition, and it thinks in random segments and in big-picture, holistic processes. It is the seat of imagination, creativity, and breakthrough concepts. It is not bound by rules or formulas. It is where dreams reside and where visions are created. The right brain recognizes possibilities that the left doesn't. The right brain experiences what the left brain receives through all of the body's senses. It works in a state of being where functioning is occurring below awareness, below the level of conscious thinking. Your creative brain is functioning 24 hours a day, processing and storing information and most importantly creating reality of the dominant thought patterns that its conscious half believes to be true.

The right brain has been called many names: "the silent mind," "the unconscious mind," "the creative mind," "the soul," to name a few, and it has been credited with magical powers, the creation of miracles, and access to infinite knowledge. Some purport to be able to receive thoughts from other minds and to have the power to attract the dominant desire of the left brain it is housed with. Your creative brain has many jobs and is already working tirelessly every hour of the day and night to deliver solutions to your assignments. It wants meaningful direction from your conscious thinking to execute the vast powers it has for creative challenges. When not consciously assigned it executes what it believes you want by your actions and dominant thoughts, both positive and negative.[2]

Our task as inventors is to improve the use of habitual conscious thinking directed to the creative brain and the use of images and conscious assignments to direct your creative brain toward specific goals related to your inventive problems.

My intent is not to fully define the science of conscious and creative brain thinking. My goal is to share the methods on how to use the two-brain thinking concept to create inventive solutions. I have experienced the positive effects of applying well-documented techniques to engage the creative mind into delivering unexpected and unexplainable results. I am a believer in the power contained in the creative mind and will share how I feel you can use it to further your inventive efforts.

2 I credit Sigmund Freud with much of this information on the conscious and subconscious brains and their functioning, but thousands of sources have since added or detracted from the original works of Freud. Many have tried to disprove the existence of two-brain thinking and functioning; however, the fact remains that the original concepts live on and are proven by actions and results of countless exercises in many studies and stories about the success that two-brain thinking has achieved.

## INTRODUCING THE CREATIVE THOUGHT PROCESS

You can only realize your full potential as an inventor if your conscious and creative brains work together toward your goal. The following exercises will help you develop cooperative mind functions, but before we get to that, I want to address the skepticism and doubt that often accompany any talk of using your mental powers to accomplish results that defy logical expectations.

I believe we don't hear much about the creative powers of right-brain mental process because it can sound a lot like magic or mystical malarkey. Our rational minds can often reject the power of creative mind techniques because they just don't seem real or reasonable. For those who cultivate this power, and have experienced the results of creative mind techniques, the understanding is far greater because experience makes it real. But if a rational-minded individual rules out the potential of tapping into creative mind communication, the experience isn't recognized and therefore is easily dismissed.

One of the greatest discoveries you can ever make in life is that you control your own circumstances through thought. You control the outcomes of all you attempt, and by leveraging the power of your creative brain, you can obtain whatever it is you truly desire if it is in the realm of possibility (and if you believe you can).

There are obviously things that you cannot accomplish in this way; this is where reality and uncontrollable circumstances come in. You cannot grow a second head or prevent a hurricane from happening by your thought process. What you seek through the use of your creative brain has to be believable and achievable.

When you realize how powerful your creative mind force really is and you begin to use your thoughts for positive results, it will change your life. This goes way beyond invention, but since we are in this inventing journey together, it's a perfect place to begin.

• • •

## THOUGHT TO CONTROL OUTCOMES

The exploration of the power of thought to control the outcomes of your life can be traced back to ancient times. It can be argued that outside influence on creative (subconscious) thinking that was not fully understood was attributed to influences from gods in some cultures. Hindu texts (the Vedas) explored unconscious aspects of mentality as far back as 2500 BC.

The Tao and the Bible have references to your ability to use thought to improve the circumstances of your life and to accomplish great achievements.

In the Bible, a statement is made that indicated that belief in the deeper mind has the power of delivering your requests if you believe fully in the power of your mind.

"Truly I tell you, if you say to this mountain, 'Be taken up and thrown into the sea,' and if you do not doubt in your heart but believe that what you say will come to pass, it will be done for you. So I tell you, whatever you ask in prayer, believe that you have received it, and it will be yours" (Mark 11:23–24, NRSV). Belief is the key principle here; if you try to use your creative mind powers of the subconscious (creative brain) but don't truly believe it will work, it won't. So prove it to yourself in small steps, then the full power of creation will be yours.

The American philosopher and psychologist William James was the first educator to teach a psychology course. One quote attributed to James on the power of thought is: "And where faith in a fact can help create the fact." And Spencer W. Kimball, the twelfth president of the Church of Jesus Christ of Latter-day Saints, wrote in *The Miracle of Forgiveness*: "Man alone, of all creatures on earth, can change his thought pattern and become the architect of his destiny."

Belief and attitude are both products of applied thought. While James and Kimball didn't delve here into the conscious and subconscious aspects of our minds, they do teach the belief of being able to change your life and create desired outcomes by applied thought.

James Allen, a lesser-known philosopher of the early 1900s, went much further in his writings on the power of mental application. I quote from his most popular work, *As a Man Thinketh*: "Tempest-tossed souls, wherever ye may be, under whatsoever conditions ye may live, know this—in the ocean of life the isles of Blessedness are smiling, and the sunny shore of your ideal awaits your coming. Keep your hand firmly upon the helm of thought. In the back of your soul[3] reclines the commanding Master; He does but sleep; wake Him."

Toward the end of his arguments in *As a Man Thinketh*, Allen sums up that thought is your controlling power, and with the applied Master-power (subconscious), your ideal can be accomplished. This small book is filled with many profound arguments supporting the power of thought to create. Here is one more from Allen: "You will become as small as your controlling desire; as great as your dominant aspiration."

Napoleon Hill spent 20 years studying highly successful people and claimed Andrew Carnegie as his inspiration and mentor when writing his classic *Think and Grow Rich*, which incorporates his findings into 16 laws of success. First published in 1937 by the Ralston Society, the book is still in print today and has sold over 20 million copies. Hill writes about the use of the subconscious and of autosuggestion to accomplish your goals. One of the most important key ideas from Hill's work is that whatever your mind can "conceive and believe, the mind can achieve."

There are now hundreds of books on the power of the subconscious creative brain; some are comprehensive studies by acclaimed professionals and others are more mystic in nature. For our purposes, I ask only that you approach the steps to your inventive process with an open mind and give them a try. They will work for you, as they have worked for me and for countless others given effort, persistence, and a little belief.

## STIMULATING COOPERATIVE MIND FUNCTIONING

We have discussed the functions of the conscious and subconscious mind and the power of the creative mind to work with the conscious mind to accomplish your inventive goals. At many times and in many ways, the left and right hemispheres work together seamlessly and

3 Our subconscious (creative) mind has often been referred to as our soul.

without conscious thought, such as when you meet someone you are acquainted with and are searching to recall who this person is: the right is assessing the visual and the left is assessing the voice and what is being said to identify your acquaintance. You are not aware of the two processes going on, but you receive the result of this brain cooperation.

On the other hand, communication between the two brains is sometimes easy and sometimes not. Betty Edwards in her classic book *Drawing on the Right Side of the Brain* comments that the left brain, the communicator or conscious part of your brain, is dominant and often suppresses the creative brain. The creative brain doesn't really care to fight back; it goes about its business behind the consciousness. Edwards offers the tactic of tricking your left brain by "providing it with a task that it will turn down" and thereby opening access directly to the creative (right) brain. For example, in her lessons on drawing, you trick the left brain by drawing upside down or by focusing on negative spaces instead of positive spaces, both concepts that don't make sense to the conscious brain and are therefore rejected. I've done this in a course on upside-down drawing taught by one of Edwards's advocates, and my left brain tuned out. My drawing was much better (not great, but better). In idea generation techniques, there are multiple exercises that accomplish a similar reaction between conscious and creative that stimulate a greater level of cooperative mind functioning. I will introduce some of these to you shortly.

People use both sides of their brain. Different people tap into traits of either the left or right brain more than others (being left-brain or right-brain dominant). But few people control the communications between the two brains, which is what unlocks cooperative mind functioning.

Your creative mind is your greatest partner in achieving inventive success. By mastering and using a few techniques of communicating to your right brain and requesting the support you need, you can harness the full power of inventive creation that resides in your brain.

Based on one principle of cooperative mind functioning, which has been touted in many success strategies over centuries, any idea dominantly occupying your conscious mind can turn into reality through the solution delivery processes of the creative mind. The goal is for the conscious mind to deliver deliberate instructions to the creative mind, repeatedly.

## MESSAGING THE CREATIVE MIND

Consistent repetition is an exercise to reinforce what you want to convey to your subconscious.

The term "autosuggestion," meaning messaging to yourself in a way to influence self-development, it is an effective way of communicating with your creative mind. It was first used as a psychological technique by Émile Coué de la Châtaigneraie, an apothecary at the beginning of the 20th century. Coué developed a method of positive reinforcement, which he taught to his clients. He began with hypnosis but realized that not everyone could be hypnotized and many did not retain the suggestions delivered directly to the subconscious brain upon awakening. This led him to develop his method of conscious self-suggestion, explained in his first book, *Self Mastery Through Conscious Autosuggestion.*

Coué's self-suggestion, self-hypnosis, and more modern techniques such as meditation, visualization, and administered hypnosis are all methods used to directly communicate with the creative mind. Generally, repetition of a single request or direction is required for the creative mind to accept that this message is indeed something intended for creative mind action. The more emotionally powerful your request or direction, the more impact it has on the creative mind. The creative mind is very sensitive to emotion. The more the conscious mind believes that this request is real, that it is necessary, and that it will occur, the more powerful the reaction of your creative mind.

Begin with a daily communication that recognizes the strengths of the right brain and affirms them, then follow with a detailed request for the particular input (or action, idea, or occurrence) you are seeking and a statement of belief that you know this will happen. Repeating your communication will fortify the belief in your consciousness and over time your creative brain will believe you and deliver what you are seeking. You are communicating with your creative brain and through repetition reinforcing your belief in the results you will receive by creating this relationship.

If you have been ignoring the power of your right brain for years, it probably won't respond to this communication practice with a first attempt. You must continue this and strengthen your belief that at the right moment what you request will be received and acted upon in some fashion.

Your message needs to be delivered when the right (quiet) brain is receptive.

Sometimes it doesn't listen. The right brain isn't really interested during the high-energy, go-go-get-it-done part of your day (unless your energy is directed to right brain communications at that time). For cooperative mind functioning to be effective, your messaging is best delivered when the mind is in a quiet receptive state, generally immediately before sleep and immediately upon arising are good times. Your subconscious has been in control during the sleep hours and is most receptive during these times. Messaging following meditation can also be very effective. You can add or create other times as you progress.

There are a few important techniques to follow in preparing your conscious message to the creative brain:

- Always phrase your message in a positive manner; negativity will shut down the creative brain functions.
- Always use the first person; you are talking to yourself; this is about you.
- Avoid using any time demands; the creative mind will determine the timeline.
- Always write out your message before delivering it so that you can be exact with each delivery. Write your message clearly and convey it to your creative mind.

Creating your communications will evolve as your inventive project evolves. You will want to focus your requests on what's missing in your direction toward an inventive solution. You might begin with the effort of identifying a problem, then in seeking an idea for a solution. Your communications will later evolve into identifying the missing piece that is a unique solution that pulls your total effort together.

It is useful to convey your request or direction in multiple ways; this helps the message to be fully received by the creative brain. The more senses involved, the more effective your communication will be. The mind sees your message when you read it; read it aloud so the brain can hear the message, too. Another useful technique is to watch yourself reading your message out loud in front of a mirror. By doing this you're now involving sight combined with sound, which has the power of reinforcement to your creative brain. A simple example of a creative mind communications is below:

> Creative brain, I need your guidance. I am searching for a unique solution to the problem of instant water heating. I need a solution that avoids maintaining hot elements or methods of heat transfer, in order to conserve energy. I know there is a method to do this, but I need your help to identify it. Please guide me to this solution. Thank you.

In your mind's eye, see yourself already in possession of this solution as you read your statement. What will you be doing with it? Work on your vision of seeing yourself with the solution. Reassure yourself following the reading that you believe the results will come. Repetition breeds belief and results; keep at it. By the way, "thank you" is appreciated by the subconscious; it seldom gets recognized as the provider of answers and solutions, and you want a good working relationship between your conscious and subconscious. A little thank-you can go a long way.

If this all seems awkward, the best thing is to just accept that it is and keep doing it; it will be less awkward in a short while. Know that it works and will be worth getting over this feeling.

Through repetition you are not only reinforcing the message to your creative brain, you're also allowing your conscious mind to grow in its belief in the results and to grow more emotionally involved in the delivery of the message.

When you are comfortable with your message, begin to add in a period of time daily where you sit quietly, perhaps in a dimmed room, perhaps with gentle acoustic music playing or a sound machine. Close your eyes. Breathe in deeply, filling your lungs to capacity, then round your lips and slowly blow out this air to capacity and repeat six to ten times, relaxing your mind and body on each breath. As you do this, visualize in your mind's eye the answer you are looking for, imagine what it looks like, how it feels (emotionally and physically). Ask for a vision of your solution, accept everything that comes to mind, and just keep going. At first you may not receive much, but keep at it and believe.

When you're feeling skeptical, just remember this is a time-proven method of great accomplishments used by great men and women for centuries. Creative mind messaging has proven successful and you can enjoy its benefits to accomplish what you desire if you practice repeated communication on a regular basis.

As you repeatedly engage your creative brain in this fashion, your results will come easier and faster. It's like you are strengthening a muscle; you need to use it, stretch it, and use it again. Over time it will serve you as a strong supporter.

Here are a few simple examples of messaging communications:

> With your help, creative brain, I am progressing toward becoming a lifetime inventor. Since we are in cooperative communications, I believe you will deliver opportunities and solutions for inventing and make them accessible to me. Please make me aware of a problem that needs an inventive solution. Thank you, creative mind.

Another version of the same request:

> I have you, my creative force, in me. I know you will cooperate with my consciousness to identify the one challenge that is uniquely mine to solve with an inventive solution. I believe the challenge and solution will appear through my communications

with you, my subconscious brain, and will be worthy of our efforts. Thank you, creative mind.

I am confident that my creative power, which resides in my subconscious brain, will work with my consciousness to reveal the answers needed to design and develop a comprehensive solution to monitor hygiene practices in patient rooms without interfering with the care of the patient. I have done a year's worth of research and have the data to work with; the solution is important to saving lives by preventing hospital-acquired infections. The ultimate solution will involve multiple unique aspects working together. Please, creative brain, guide me to the answers on this important effort. Thank you.

Resulted in US Patent 9,542,663: Multi-tag identification devices, variable-power standoff readers for same, and related systems.

## CREATE A COOPERATIVE MIND ALLIANCE

For inventing, I encourage developing a cooperative mind alliance through perfecting brain-to-brain communications and cooperation. To invent, both brains need the services of the other. At first the left brain may still try to dominate, but as long as it has a goal of working cooperatively with the creative brain for the common good an alliance can be established.

So how do we accomplish this alliance? It will take practice and patience and constant repetition. It's not really hard. It begins with your left brain talking directly to the right brain daily as described earlier. To get at its treasure of creative input, the right brain must believe that the left brain really wants the input; the belief must be real. How do you do this?

Joseph Murphy, PhD, DD, in his book *The Power of Your Subconscious Mind*, relates how the author of *Treasure Island*, *Strange Case of Dr. Jekyll and Mr. Hyde*, and *Kidnapped*, among others, Robert Louis Stevenson, would assign his creative mind the charge of delivering a good marketable story before retiring for sleep. Stevenson usually did this when his bank account was low. Stevenson recounted that his creative mind would provide a new story piece by piece in more or less a serial fashion until the story was complete. He had developed his cooperative mind practice to deliver just what he needed when he needed it most and simply asked for it.

You can accomplish your inventive goals by taking full conscious control of the directive messages that you send to you creative brain. When a directive is implanted as truth in the creative brain, the creative brain immediately starts to cause conditions, actions, and circumstances to occur that will lead to accomplishing the direction. The creative brain begins to attract what is needed to perform the assignments and deliver the results the conscious brain desires. It will give to the consciousness all the tools, answers, ideas, and secrets needed. The consciousness must only recognize these gifts, act on them, and the rewards will be received. With a little success, the process will become habitual, like it was with Robert Louis Stevenson; both minds will be rewarded and it will be hard to stop the process.

**POINTS TO REMEMBER**

1. If you focus your conscious thinking long enough on one particular problem and fuel the thinking with adequate study and research, your creative brain mental process will guide or lead you toward the new and unique solution you are seeking, provided you are communicating with your subconscious and looking for the responses.
2. As soon as your subconscious mind accepts the assignment you have provided, it begins to put everything into action to make it happen and to attract the tools, associations, and ideas you need to execute the solution.
3. Inventing is a process of thinking followed by a process of doing (or multiple periods of each). Training your thought processes to cooperate on the left and right brain functions, each performing what they do best, can be accomplished with practice and the help of mental exercise.
4. Things that don't yet exist first appear in the right (creative) brain. Consciously assigning the responsibility for a problem

solution to your right brain and requesting a solution will bring results. Repeat the request until the solution shows up. It is mandatory that you communicate with your creative brain regularly and in a positive directive way to achieve the inventive results you are seeking. Expect results, know that they will come, and reaffirm your objectives until they are achieved.

5. The creative mind receives messages from all senses; what it sees, feels, and hears all reinforce the conscious messages you send it. Use as many communication techniques as you can.

• CHAPTER 7 •

# Creating Inventive Ideas and Potential Solutions

**STEP 7:** Generate ideas that you can develop into inventive solutions.

**STEP 8:** Use imagination and visualization to enhance ideas.

It is in the mind of a single person that creative ideas and concepts are born.

–Mervin Joe Kelly, former president of Bell Labs

**TO MANY, THE** source of truly unique ideas is a mystery. In some European museums, you can find early seafaring charts marking spots in the oceans where magical answers reside. We can only imagine how this happened: the ancient mariner had a great idea and realized that he didn't know where the idea came from; he figured there must be a source of ideas below the ocean surface—so he marked the chart so he could come back for more.

Like the ancients believed, ideas and answers do lie below the surface, only you don't have to sail the oceans to find them. To review what we've learned in the previous chapter, part of your brain is at work 24 hours a day below the surface. The functions of your creative brain work in conjunction with your conscious brain to create ideas and solutions that get delivered at the conscious level by various means. The creative brain works on what you hold most prominent in your conscious mind:

that which you have faith and belief in and convey with emotion to your creative brain as a directive. All exercises in this chapter encourage your two brains to do what they each do best in cooperation with each other toward common goals—this is cooperative mind functioning.

At this stage in the invention creation process, I am assuming you have chosen and are committed to your particular problem to solve with invention. You have a clear, well-defined problem statement as your guide. Your research has reached a point where you are armed with a wealth of knowledge on your subject and related subjects. You know some of the challenges facing you in the next stage of creative inventing, and you are actively communicating with your creative mind to seek inventive direction and guidance. This chapter is about generating a lot of ideas pertaining to the challenges you face while inventing to solve the problem you have chosen. You will accomplish this through exercises promoting cooperation and communication between your conscious and creative minds.

Linus Pauling, an American scientist, is the only person to win two undivided Nobel Prizes, one in 1954 for his work on chemical bonds and structures of complex systems and the second in 1962 for his work opposing weapons of mass destruction. In a 1995 presentation titled "The Impact of Linus Pauling on Molecular Biology," Francis Crick quoted Pauling as saying that in order to have good ideas, it is necessary to have many of them. He states "most of them will be wrong" and that the person needs to figure out which ideas are good and which should be abandoned. In this stage of your invention process, this sums up your task quite well. With your creative and conscious minds in alliance, you will create many ideas utilizing the exercises that follow. Don't worry yet about whether or not they are good ideas; now you just want a lot of them. We will deal with enhancing and evaluating the ideas in the chapters to come.

Possibilities and solutions all start as ideas. Our mantra at my previous invention business was that "ideas enlighten, invigorate, improve, enrich, and embolden us." Your imagination is the engine of idea delivery, it is a direct communication link between the creative mind and the conscious mind. In this section, we will work on fine-tuning your brain-to-brain communication skills and how to encourage the generation of the ideas you will develop into inventions.

Cooperative brain communication generates ideas that create new possibilities for your inventive solution. You are prepared because of your research and study, guided by your problem statement, and reinforced by your communications with your creative brain. You are ready to create.

Your creative brain already has some concepts and ideas brewing, waiting to be teased out into the conscious brain. This is because you have been communicating your problem and its challenges since you first wrote your problem statement. Now you just need to pull them out into your consciousness.

To begin evaluating, developing, and testing these ideas, you need to practice ways to get all these ideas into the conscious level where you can work with them. Your work with the exercises in this chapter could reveal complete solutions, clues to follow toward a solution, or new problems that are a hidden part of your primary problem that need their own solutions. Your mind is well equipped to deal with all of these situations now.

When creating ideas, play with them to generate more ideas by creating combinations or developing related concepts from the earlier ideas. Mark Twain once said, "There is no such thing as a new idea. It is impossible. We simply take a lot of old ideas and put them into a sort of mental kaleidoscope. We give them a turn and they make new and curious combinations. We keep on turning and making new combinations indefinitely; but they are the same old pieces of colored glass that have been in use through all the ages."

The following techniques will help you communicate openly with your creative mind to generate a lot of answers or ideas. Some of the cooperative mind exercises can be used to further develop ideas into full-blown concepts and designs. I will introduce the exercises here and we will work on idea refinement in the chapters to come.

## TECHNIQUE 1: DOODLING AND SKETCHING

The creative brain loves visual communications and responds well to exercises involving all types of visual communication. Doodling and sketching seem like two similar techniques to aid visual thinking, but when applied to cooperative mind thinking, they are very different in how they work and what they accomplish.

Visual thinking is critical to inventive problem-solving, and both doodling and sketching can provide critical pieces to your inventive effort.

Doodling is rough drawing or scribbling absentmindedly. Not thinking about what is going onto the paper is the key to successful doodling. Your conscious mind is calm, resting (absent), and not tuned into what you are drawing when you are doodling. Your creative mind and your hand are doing the exercise. Your creative mind is leading the exercise. Sometime the results are visual gibberish, but at other times the creative brain provides you with key concepts or information. It is a time when the channels to the creative mind are communicating openly without interference from the conscious mind. Just let your creative mind and your hand create whatever they want on paper, tune out, and just keep going; investigate it later.

Sketching is led by your conscious mind; it starts with an idea or an objective and you apply reasoned thinking to what you are applying to paper. This is a tool where cooperation between both brains creates results, solves problems, and explores ideas. It is an excellent vehicle for cooperative mind functioning; since you are working in a visual medium, both minds are active.

Sketching is a valuable tool for visualizing your problem and its solution. Sketching communicates more directly with your creative brain and allows your creative brain to communicate to your conscious brain through your sketching process. It is a two-brain process with conscious thought applied to the drawing.

Thomas Edison could not visualize in his mind as purely as Einstein or Tesla could. Edison would sketch a lot and through his sketching feed his creative mind with problems, looking for solutions and in return creating possibilities in pictures from messages received from his creative brain.

Sketching was Edison's main method of working through new ideas and turning them into invention; he carried his sketchbook with him most of the time. Don't worry if you are not artistically inclined. Imperfect sketching can actually be preferable to detailed sketching as it allows the creative brain to fill in the rough edges and recognize possibilities.

Computer-aided design (CAD) modeling, where your focus is more on executing the software rules for creating drawing or modeling work, is not an acceptable substitute for sketching. With CAD, the work is mostly left brain work and therefore does not involve the same mental processes. It does little to connect the work of your two minds. The creative mind tends to tune out with software execution of this process; it wants to be more spontaneous. Hand sketching combines the use of both mind hemispheres providing back-and-forth results. A sketch also calls for continued thinking and development. Move from one sketch to another and compare the results. Break off pieces and detail the components of your sketch. Occasionally put the sketching aside and do other work; when you come back to them, look at them for clues to new ideas or more detailed solutions. Eventually the ideas you want will take shape. As you sketch, ask "what if" questions and then fill in the sketch with the result.

## TECHNIQUE 2: VERBALIZATION

Another technique used by inventors to create ideas through mind cooperation and improve communications between their two minds is the process of verbalizing your problem and asking the creative brain for ideas. The technique is to talk out loud to yourself about your problem in detail using descriptive, visual language (a left-brain exercise). The verbal sounds connect your creative processes; as your ears hear what you are saying, the message is registered directly in your creative mind. This aids in making your conscious and creative mind a team to work together to solve your problem. This method is chronicled by Evan Schwartz in his book *Juice* when he introduces Woody Norris, a modern-day independent inventor best known for his invention of the transcutaneous Doppler system for listening to blood vessel movement. Norris says talking out loud helps the brain focus on one direction from "all these different, disconnected things vying for its attention." This technique then narrows the message to your creative mind to a single assignment (a dominant thought) with which it is free to deliver a solution. Too many messages and the creative brain will go about its other chores, waiting for a clearer message from your consciousness.

## TECHNIQUE 3: MIND MAPPING

A great way to generate ideas using cooperative mind communications is to learn to use mind mapping. This is among the best tools for idea generation and detailing because it combines the imaginative part of your creative brain and the logical part of your conscious brain in visual communication. The imaginative part visualizes the total picture delivering ideas and the logical part works on the details. Tomasz Arciszewski in his book *Inventive Engineering* describes mind mapping as "a visual representation of a body of knowledge related to a specific concept." A mind map shows how the main concept is related to other concepts in a nonlinear, visual illustration. In the illustration, the main concept inhabits the middle of a web of related concepts that are connected to it via lines (of varying thickness) signifying their relationship to one another. A mind map is most effective when produced using a variety of visual cues such as different fonts, colors, pictures, abstract shapes, etc.

You should hand draw mind maps. Mind mapping software programs exist, but I believe the largest benefit of mind mapping is the direct communication between your conscious and creative mind that happens when your hands, eyes, and mind are working together. This doesn't work as well when executing computer program rules. A mind map becomes a visual map of everything relative to your inventive problem.

Tony Buzan is credited as the developer of the mind map technique and has written several books on the subject. A good place to start is with *How to Mind Map*, though his concepts were originally presented in a 1994 study of the same name. The process has become a movement in what is currently termed "whole brain thinking," which we call "a cooperative mind alliance." The power of mind mapping, or whole brain thinking, for inventing is underexplored, in my opinion, but if you practice the process, you will possess a tool that will provide many clues to your eventual inventive solutions. I will outline my process to get you started.

I usually work at a table with access to a write-on/wipe-off and magnetic white board. On the white board, I write the purpose of my mind map in big letters, usually in different colors. For example: "What will I invent next?" (Usually I try to be more specific to a particular invention project.) If I have pictures, drawings, clippings, or other visual aids, I put them on the board with magnets.

I have at least a dozen markers and pens, and I always have colored pencils and even crayons handy. I recently added highlighters for shading instead of crayons.

On the table I lay out a large blank sheet of white paper, sometimes flip chart paper with a sticky top or I tape the corners to the table. In the center of the paper I draw a picture or diagram of the central theme or a colorful elaborate word that represents the exercise—"My Invention" for example. On lines radiating out from the central theme in multiple directions (colorful and different designed lines) I write key words (or draw them as pictures); there may be 5 or 6 lines, but no rules apply. I will use "water," "heat," "hygiene," "sensing," "steam," and "venting" as these are all areas I have invented in before and therefore I have specialized knowledge accumulated in these areas. I add a line "what else."

Don't worry about anything being right or drawn well or making sense. Just going with the flow is critical.

Now for any one of the key words that strikes me I draw multiple lines coming out and add associated words. For "water" I add, "heating," "cooling," "filtering," "carbonating," "swimming" (don't know why). For "heat" I add "resistance," "exchange," "Ohmic" (a method of heating); for "hygiene" I add "gloves," "sensing," "hands," "environment" and so on.

With no pre-determined direction my mind will start to break down one of the key word extensions, for example (water) –heating, and I draw multiple lines coming from "heating" and add "buildings," "localized," "sinks," "exchange," "Ohmic," "infrared," etc.

Just keep going until all your thoughts have been diagrammed on the map.

When you feel that you have exhausted everything you can come up with at the time, then it is time to examine relationships between your free-flow thinking.

Some unintended patterns emerged for me. The words "water," "heating," "Ohmic," "infrared," and perhaps "spaces" take me in a direction of a water heating system for spaces. Similar to my experience, you might find you have repeated words or have close associations between words that reveal themes or directions.

I circle (or frame, or star) what I feel are connected words in a theme and connect them with lines. If there is a flow relationship I will note it with arrowheads on some lines. In one fashion or another group these words on a new line, in a frame below the original map, and put them in order if that seems appropriate.

Water
Heating Methods
    Ohmic, Exchange (types of heat generation)
    Local
    Sinks

An idea had formed and I added "sinks" and "local" to my list and eliminated "space." My pattern changed my direction to heating water at sinks, locally (meaning at each individual sink).

Mind maps can go on through the course of your inventive process over multiple periods of time, or they might never be done. If you do create a mind map it can be complete when you have achieved your ultimate objective. Until then, you'll be generating ideas every step of the way.

Periodically during a project I will return to the map and add to it. Some I know of do this daily and use a mind map as the primary tool for an entire project.

You will find that as you consciously work on creating the mind map unexpected words, thoughts, and directions will pop into your conscious effort. These are the creative mind inputs—cherish them, use them. These are ideas to explore.

I tend to use more words than pictures and diagrams, but it works for me. Take some time to view and study some really detailed and elaborate mind maps to see the extent these can be used. A good place to start is https://www.mindmapart.com; it is a showcase of the world's finest mind maps.

## TECHNIQUE 4: STREAM OF CONSCIOUSNESS

Another idea-generating technique is a stream-of-consciousness session. These are powerful exercises for linking conscious and creative mind thinking. The term was introduced by William James in his *Principles of Psychology*. Introduced as an exercise for creative thinking with a particular topic or problem to address, a stream-of-consciousness session is when you write thoughts, feelings, ideas, and reactions in a continuous uninterrupted flow with no critique or consideration for what ends up on paper. For my purposes, I conduct sessions with a time limit and a set goal for the number of thought entries I write. I number each idea or thought. The numbering obviously counts the number of thoughts or ideas but also is used when assessing or grouping various ideas after the exercise.

In my stream-of-consciousness exercises, I will sit with my notebook and a timer and execute an exercise of writing (and sometimes sketching) for 15 minutes, as fast as I can go, without any thought to the results. I begin with a heading—for example, "Define Characteristics of a Point of Use, Sink Water Heater"—and I try to get to at least 50 notes before my timer expires. The faster you go without applying any conscious thought to each entry, the better your results will be.

When I reread my list I look for associations, eliminate anything that is random, and combine items that are similar. Usually I will have a short list of meaningful, useful data related to my exercise. I will expand this data with relevant descriptions.

For my example of the sink heater, I ended up with the edited, enhanced list below:

- Small (easily fit under a bathroom sink)
- Retrofit (biggest market)
- Do-it-yourself kit
- 120 volt
- Ohmic heated (heat water volumetrically)
- Eliminate current leakage (a problem with Ohmic heating)
- Grounding (create a new method for flowing water)
- Exchange matter (sand, graphite)
- Possibly ceramic (instead of sand)
- End cap membranes smaller than particles
- Find specific mix percentage needed (test various mixtures of materials)
- Titanium electrode plates (conductive coating) (a design is coming together)
- Replaceable (components, electrodes)
- Flow control (energize electrodes when flow starts) (details are emerging)

These four techniques are for generating a lot of thoughts or ideas to advance your thinking toward an inventive solution. There are others and you will find what works best for you, or mix it up and use them all, but either way you will have a lot of ideas associated with your inventive problem through these exercises. In each method, you are encouraging communications between the conscious and creative minds to reveal combined thinking ideas. Ideas are not solutions; they are potential solutions, and you then need to explore and discard the ones that won't work and detail and expand the ones you want to take forward toward invention.

The next exercises are more cognitive and less free-flowing. Practicing these thinking techniques will expand your understanding of how to turn your ideas into unique inventions.

The following techniques are for expanding on some of your ideas. They will be useful to clarify some confusing ideas and will continue to be useful in problem-solving and design throughout your entire inventive process.

## TECHNIQUE 5: IMAGINATION

I list imagination as a technique here; however, it is much more than that. All ideas and inventive solutions are generated from the imagination. Albert Einstein once stated the "imagination is more important than knowledge." He went on to state that knowledge is limited (and the imagination is not). All invention originates in the imagination.

I believe that the imagination is a two-way conduit for communication between the subconscious creative mind and the conscious, logical planning mind. It is where both the conscious mind and the creative mind communicate in images. It is where images can be exchanged, modified, and enhanced. It is where the conscious mind can insert images of what exists, what the challenge may be, and begin to play with ideas of what could be by changing or combining concepts with images. It is where the creative mind can insert images and visions conveying new ideas and solutions to the consciousness (without having to talk).

The conscious mind can initiate a period of imagining whenever it chooses. The creative mind is seeing all the conscious imagining and will often toss in a piece of the puzzle in the form of a new image, vision, insight, or entire solution.

The work you have been doing with messaging your creative mind is the key that opens cooperative mind functioning and the imagination is the vehicle the creative mind most often uses to deliver what you are requesting. The combination of creative mind messaging and conscious use of your imagination to stimulate conversations with your creative mind results in invention (when this is your objective).

Most everyone is born with a very active imagination that tends to slow down as we age, probably because we don't use it as much. In my story earlier of attacking three-masted galleys, we could see our enemies, the galley, and the gold vividly in our imagination as we ran screaming across the sand dunes. As children, imagining comes easily, and we create the world we want around us in the moment. Creative mind messaging will reawaken your imagination to create the results you want to successfully invent.

Napoleon Hill, in his classic 1937 book *Think and Grow Rich*, called the imagination the "workshop of the mind." By this he is indicating that the conscious brain receives direct input from the imagination (most often communications from the creative brain) to accomplish the achievements directed by the conscious mind. All new things first exist in someone's imagination and it has been said that "if you can imagine it, you can create it" (attributed to the writer William Arthur Ward). To stimulate image activity in my creative mind, I use pictures, clippings from magazines, drawings, sketches, doodles, simple models, and the like to convert thoughts into pictures. Some pictures that are pertinent are hung on my wall; others I flip through in a file folder as I imagine how to solve the current problem. These include the drawings I have found with patents. Another method is to play with parts and pieces of just about anything, assembling or disassembling into a simple prototype that your mind can see as a clue to answers you are looking for. These are all ways to message your creative mind and stimulate imagination activity.

When beginning a development for Apple around 1982, an employee of David Kelley Design (later IDEO) was seeking inspiration while trying to imagine how to adapt a computer mouse, first invented in 1964 by Douglas C. Engelbart but not widely accepted, to serve the needs of Apple users. He wandered across the street to a Walgreens store, needing a prop to help imagine a solution. Jim Yurchenco bought a butter dish and put the top over a small ball, creating a simple prototype—and the computer mouse was born. The butter dish and ball image morphed into the first mass-produced computer mouse in history and has been called "the most lovable icon of the computer age."

In conscious imagining, we begin thinking about the problem, what we know, and then think about what might be. We look at clues in images or props and the creative mind sees an opening when you arrive at the "might be" part and what can happen in a cooperative mind communication that delivers a solution or a piece of a solution to your consciousness. The more prepared the creative brain is with assignments (through messaging) prior to periods of imagining, the more the solutions will occur. These are imagination sessions and you will use them throughout your invention process.

In your imagination sessions, play with your challenges; study them to see what works and what doesn't. Try to create something entirely new from your observations and your experiences. Try imagining different items combined into something new. What might that produce? This kind of thinking gets you using the imagination tool and will help you develop the habit of using the imagination for solution creation. Think of using your imagination to create a dream or a movie, put pictures together, move them around, see what happens to this piece or that; you are playing with your problem and encouraging your creative brain to participate.

## TECHNIQUE 6: VISUALIZATION

Visualization is a tool to aid your imagination and can be honed and improved as you use the skill. When you can create pictures with your conscious mind, you enhance the results that your creative brain will deliver. Through visualization your creative mind produces pictures for your conscious mind to interpret so that it knows more thoroughly what is expected in return. In Carlson's biography, Nicola Tesla said he was inspired by the following saying, which he attributed to Isaac Newton and which talks about his ability to generate unique ideas: "I simply hold the thought steadily in my mind's eye (seeing a picture) until clear light dawns upon me." He thought deeply on his problem until the creative brain projected a mental image of a solution recognized by his conscious brain.

Tesla was perhaps the greatest natural visualizer in the golden age of inventors. He was born with a powerful visual imagination, which was so dominant that he sometimes could not tell the difference between what was real and what his imagination generated. He could see complete models of his inventions before they existed. Sometimes he would visualize the products his inventions were to replace, watch them run, see where the problems were, and then visually correct them. Tesla claimed that the entire image for how to make an alternating current motor came to him unexpectedly in a moment of visualization while reciting poetry in a park. He immediately drew the solution in the sand with a stick for a friend who was walking with him.

If your problem is such that there are pictures and images that depict the problem, hang them up or put them in a notebook and look at them daily. Think of the boards of photographs and data that show up on crime show episodes; the boards are visually implanting information to the crime-solver's creative brain so it can work on and deliver an answer to the crime. Your creative brain is visual, so provide all you can in picture form. There are several techniques that will aid you in improving your ability to visualize; practice each to see what works best for you.

## Practicing Visualization

Every one of us has the ability to close our eyes and conjure up pictures and scenes of just about whatever we choose. With practice and repetition, we can use this ability as a powerful tool to stimulate imagination activity and cooperative mind communication.

To practice visualization, periodically take your problem into a quiet dark room, free from any distractions. Sit comfortably, close your eyes, and think in pictures; project them onto your mind's eye. Think of a projector sending a picture onto a screen. Start with what you know and can see as an image related to your problem; try turning it and looking at the image from all angles. You are not trying to force a solution, you are just studying what you know. As you progress, ask yourself some questions: How can I make this happen? Can I replace this with . . . ?

After a while try assembling a mental solution to your problem. Much of your physical design for a problem solution can be drawn inside your head before you ever touch a screen or piece of paper. Don't be discouraged if you can't execute this perfectly the first time you try; it takes practice. The practice will be worth the effort. If you have trouble forming visual images, you can use models. Artists do this all the time. Your model may be a real thing that has some similarities to your visual exercise or drawings or photographs. Google Images is a tremendous help to me when I begin a visual exercise. Study the model or image you find, even stare at it for a period of time—say, a minute—and then close your eyes to see if you can see it in your mind's eye. Try again; it will help.

In his biography of Einstein, Walter Isaacson explained that Einstein imagined he was a beam of light traveling through space. He could create a vision of himself riding alongside the light beam, allowing him to study the electromagnetic field. This vision, at age 16, was instrumental in his development of the theory of special relativity (ten years later).

Try pretending that you are your problem or a product of your problem. In the character of your problem, ask some questions: How do I feel? What would I say if asked to improve myself? How do others see me? Where are my weaknesses?

This kind of thinking gets your mind to look at your problem from a different perspective: the problem's perspective. The results can be impressive and are often received in an unexpected form.

Einstein and Tesla were great visualizers. Einstein could see himself riding that beam of light and make calculations on travel time from Earth to the moon. Einstein challenged his subconscious, practicing with what he called *Gedanken* experiments (German for "thought experiments"). Working as a patent examiner, he would often go on daydream trips, with what he stated as ideas that he twirled around in his head rather than in a lab. His process usually began with something real, some event or thing where he could then ask questions and modify what was real or understandable into thoughts of "what if" or a series of "I wonder" thoughts. He once daydreamed that he was a painter and fell off a roof. He wondered if it would seem like the ground was coming to him instead of him falling to the ground. Then he went further and wondered what it would be like to fall through the ground to the center of the earth. Would he feel weightless there? Would he know what direction he was moving? Einstein's thought experiments often lived with him for quite some time and became pieces of his great accomplishments. This mind experiment caused him to question gravity as a universal force and led to thoughts on warps in space-time.

Visualization can be a lot like daydreaming, something for which we are so often criticized in our younger years and in school. Now is the time to pull it back out, dust it off, and get as good at it as when you were a child.

How do you stimulate your powers of visualization to get more detailed? There is no shortcut to getting really good at visualization. If you practice daydreaming and some of the techniques discussed in this chapter, you will find that it improves the more you use it. Set aside some time daily to work on daydreaming, visualizing, and imagining, and you will be light-years closer to your invention goals.

## TECHNIQUE 7: MEDITATION

Meditation is the most powerful of all the techniques to join the strengths and powers of your two brain hemispheres. In its simplest form, meditation is the balancing of both brain hemispheres in a way that allows them to work in harmony. It is a pure form of cooperative brain functioning.

The practice of meditation takes many forms and can become a lifelong learning process to perfect. On the other hand, you can experience benefit from your very first effort at a simple meditation.

The first stages of meditation are unlike your messaging to your creative brain; it is performed without a defined purpose or objective. It is a process where you train your conscious mind to become calm and your creative brain to feel welcome. It is not trying to clear your mind of thought but to focus your thinking on one particular thing or function, like breathing. As your mind wanders (and everyone's does) and you recognize its wandering, you simply bring it back to your focus.

I found an app that provides guided meditations that are very useful for this stage of meditation. You can download it and choose from a wide variety of meditations. An initial collection of over 7,000 meditations, music, and talks on meditation are available for free at https://www.insighttimer.com, and with the fee-based version over 3,000,000 guided meditations are available.

With some experience, you will train yourself to enter a meditative state very quickly and then you can continue your state of meditation directly into a cognitive session of messaging your creative brain or working on a problem solution or a visualization exercise or, as many inventors do, a mental modeling session (see below). You will find that your cognitive powers and creative insights will improve greatly as you practice and apply this technique. Solutions will pop into your consciousness (usually after meditation, not during). I have also found that a doodling session or a stream-of-consciousness exercise following meditation can be very productive.

## TECHNIQUE 8: WALKING (OR MOVING) MEDITATION

This is my preferred mind time. I walk several days a week and my wife and I (and usually friends) take at least one self-guided village-to-village long-distance walking trip annually. I find my alone time with my thoughts or just being mindful of my surroundings provides the type of cooperative mind thinking that benefits my work. Meditation while walking even has a name: in its pure form, it is called *kinhin* and has evolved from Zen meditation. My walks vary in that some are for clearing the mind; these are more meditative. Other times I work on a particular piece of my current problem. If I have a day or time when I am having trouble doing either, then I use a mantra, repeating the word or statement or sound over and over during the walk. I like using the mantra made famous by Émile Coué, whom I mentioned earlier as the pioneer of autosuggestion: "Every day in every way I am getting better and better." It has a nice rhythmic pattern and can match a walking or jogging gait.

Many great achievers were meditative walkers; among them are Aristotle, William Wordsworth, Charles Dickens, Søren Kierkegaard, James Allen, Ludwig Van Beethoven, Henry David Thoreau, John Muir, and my favorite walker, Charles Darwin. In his biographical novel *The Origin*, Irving Stone tells how Darwin built a walking trail on his property so he could walk and contemplate daily. Darwin would become so engrossed in his thoughts or meditations that he would forget how many times he had walked the path and how much time had passed. To control this without making it part of his conscious thinking, he would carry a pocket full of stones, and each time he found himself at the beginning, he would drop a stone on the pile until he ran out. In this way he knew to end his walking session after a certain number of times around his path.

By experimenting with the various techniques in this chapter, you will develop the techniques that work best for you. The results of a close working relationship between your conscious and creative brains will generate a lot of options and ideas for your problem's inventive solution. With every use of one of these techniques, you are further developing your cooperative mind messaging skills, working toward a cooperative mind alliance where you can consciously ask your subconscious for a solution and your creative brain will provide it.

While these exercises can serve you in many ways, your inventive step in this chapter is to generate a list of possible solution ideas to your inventive problem so you can further develop them into your invention concept or theory using cooperative mind communications techniques.

• CHAPTER 8 •

# Messages from the Creative Mind

**STEP 9:** Learn to recognize and interpret messages from your creative mind.

**YOU ARE WORKING** hard to consistently communicate with your creative mind in multiple ways and asking for direction and requesting solutions to solve your inventive problem. So where are the answers? Your imagination and visualization channels provide a vehicle for communication and receiving answers, but your creative brain will determine when and how it will provide answers or clues to answers. They may come disguised or concealed.

Remember, your creative mind is nonverbal; it is silent; it is not going to communicate back to you in the fashion you may expect. Your creative mind thinks in random segments but creates fully developed processes and concepts. Solutions from your creative mind may appear fully developed or show up in pieces requiring you to assemble them in your conscious mind like a jigsaw puzzle. It's important to recognize the messages as they become conscious thoughts.

As we learned, your creative mind is visual; it functions in pictures, in visions, in dreams, and in many methods of nonverbal communication. Your efforts with exercises from the previous chapter reinforce your cooperative mind communications and stimulate response. But you may not be getting all the answers you need. Or you may not be recognizing some of the answers being delivered. By becoming more aware of alternative forms of communication that your creative mind uses, you may expedite your inventive process. Put yourself in position to recognize creative mind communications when they occur or ideally with practice, like Robert Louis Stevenson, exactly when you ask for them.

## HOW CREATIVE SOLUTIONS CAN MAKE APPEARANCES

### The Hunch

With your mind fully engaged in the problem you have chosen, it is very likely that clues for partial solutions will appear in your consciousness. These will often be puzzle pieces of a complete answer. Don't ignore them; note them, add them to notes, research them to see where they lead, and look for more. The key component will likely be missing and may hide in another form, which will reveal itself through ongoing efforts, but your hunches are important; protect them, keep them. The hunch is your incremental problem solution where eventually pieces of the answer fit together.

### Mistakes and Accidents

As you enter a stage of testing and proving your potential solutions, stay observant: as you encounter unanticipated results or when a mistake happens, often something is revealed. What is revealed is something to explore and research further, or it is an indication to change a method or completely change direction to help reveal your ultimate answer. Often the mistakes are part of your experimentation phase, so cherish them. Mistakes may be completely happenstance or they might be a method for the creative mind to interfere by delivering a leap in your development work or a breakthrough for your problem or an entirely different problem. There are a lot of instances where pure mistakes lead to breakthrough developments. Sometimes they are directly related to the problem being worked on and sometimes they are unrelated breakthroughs.

One widely noted example happened to Patsy O'Connell Sherman. Patsy worked as a chemist at 3M, where she had been assigned a project of developing a rubber material that would not deteriorate from exposure to jet aircraft fuels. During one experiment, she accidently dropped some of the mixture on her shoe. Over time her shoe became stained and dirty except for the one spot where she had spilled the experimental fluid; there it remained clean and shiny. Recognizing the possibility for a new material treatment, she consulted her notes, re-created the formula for the spilled fluid, and invented Scotchgard. Scotchgard became the most widely used stain repellent in North America.

In the early 1900s, Harry Brearley from Sheffield, England, was working on perfecting a better gun barrel. Gun barrels are "rifled" or grooved in a spiral pattern to give spin to a bullet, improving accuracy. Over time the action of a bullet spinning against the inside of a barrel will wear away layers of the barrel metal, eventually making the rifle inoperable. Brearley was a metallurgist and he believed the right alloy could prevent this wearing.

As he tried and failed time and again, he discarded his useless rifle barrels into a scrap heap. After months of failing, Brearley glanced over his pile of scrap and noticed that one of the many discarded barrels had not rusted like all the rest. This barrel remained smooth and shiny. Pulling it from the pile he studied its properties: It contained 12 percent chromium blended with the steel and carbon of the metal. The alloy released a film at the surface when exposed to oxygen. Even wiping it clean or scratching the surface resulted in a new protective film forming. While working to solve his inventive problem, Brearley had accidently invented stainless steel.

Not all mistakes result in breakthroughs! Watch for the ones you can use and be prepared with the ability to repeat your mistake to make your solution work.

## The Eureka Effect

This is a moment when a sudden discovery reveals itself and full understanding comes into your consciousness. It often happens when tied to an action unrelated to your inventive problem.

The term is attributed to Archimedes, who was a mathematician in Greece over 2,200 years ago. Archimedes was asked by the king to determine if his new crown was pure gold or if he had been cheated, as he expected, by the goldsmith by adding other metal to the gold. Archimedes struggled mentally for some time, seeking a method to measure the gold content without damaging the crown. One day when he stepped into a bathtub full of water, which spilled out over the sides, he immediately realized that the displaced water was equal to his body's volume. The full solution to the crown problem was revealed to him in an instant; he placed the crown in a basin of water, measured the water displaced and measured the weight of an equal volume of pure gold and compared it to the weight of the crown. At the moment of discovery, it is said he jumped from the tub and ran naked through the streets of his town yelling, "Eureka!" (The goldsmith had cheated.)

The eureka effect will occur when you have been fully engaged in your inventive endeavor but are at the moment removed from it and doing something entirely different. (Remember Tesla reciting poetry in the park.) It is the most dramatic of the creative mind solution delivery methods, and when it happens, you have no doubt that you have been blessed with a solution from the inner workings of your mind. The details of a eureka moment can fade quickly so stop what you are doing and document everything that came into your mind.

## SHERLOCK'S MAGIC TECHNIQUE

At this stage, you are applying techniques to come up with a unique solution that will be your invention. You may feel stuck or think that it will never happen. Feel good—you are prepared for your biggest breakthrough. Let's return to Sherlock Holmes to explain the secret technique of eureka moments.

In Sherlock Holmes's novels, this step is called the "incubation period" (followed by a solution to the crime). In *A Technique for Producing Ideas* by James Webb Young, it is called the "mental digestive process" (followed by a breakthrough thought). Other terms have been used to describe this phenomenon. In essence, your creative brain has churned through solutions and has answers for you, often fully developed solutions. You just haven't harvested them yet, and your conscious mind is mired in details without being able to tune into the creative mind's solutions.

The results of this step aren't voluntary or controllable; the step works if the prior steps have been followed. There are countless references to this magic step in biographies, histories, and even the Bible, but by most accounts it is simple: step away from your mission, forget about it for a while—hours, a day, a month—and don't even think about it. Do things that you enjoy; take a trip or play golf or tennis or chess. Just don't work on your project. Put it out of your conscious mind completely.

Holmes would smoke a pipe, listen to music, and play his violin. He would attend to his beekeeping, boxing, fencing, and reading. He would write his monographs on subjects like "the identification of tobacco types" and he composed music; anything but work on the crime.

In more than one case, Sherlock Holmes would stop right at a critical point in the investigation and drag Watson to a concert, or other venue of escape, soon to be followed by Holmes being struck with the revealing solution to the mystery: "Watson, I have it."

Einstein had breakthrough thoughts while shaving; Dean

*continued*

**Kamen, inventor of the Segway, slipped in the shower and received his eureka message that he needed to control falls, not balance his invention; Philo Farnsworth (the inventor of television) was plowing a field of potatoes when his breakthrough concept hit. If you have created a solid problem to solve, done your research, observed everything you could, made your effort your compelling mission, engaged your creative mind, and made the effort to create a lot of possible solutions–it may be time to take a break. A solution, an idea, a direction *will* appear out of nowhere when you least expect it. Be ready; write it down. The thought could be fleeting; it can come in a flash. You need only to recognize it. Don't judge the thought or any piece of it, just let it come and record it. This could be your eureka moment.**

## Dreams

Dreams are another form of visual communication from your creative mind. While you are sleeping your subconscious is working away, creating dreams that we don't fully understand the function of. Sometimes simply asking your creative mind to provide an answer to a question you ask before sleeping will result in a dream answer. Most of us easily forget our dreams soon after waking, so keep a notepad handy to jot down what you recall. Doing this on a regular basis can provide excellent input to your inventive process.

Many creative personalities are known for their catnapping and many used techniques to utilize the catnap as a tool for creative mind communications. Edison was a famous napper. He would take catnaps often multiple times daily, wherever he was: on desktops, on top of boxes in his lab, or on multiple napping lounges he had placed around his lab. His dream breaks often provided some insight to the problem he was currently working on.

Napping was a part of the creative process for Einstein, Aristotle, and Salvador Dalí as well.

Dalí believed that the first few seconds of sleep were where the maximum benefit to mind and body occurred. He used to slouch in his chair with his right hand over the side holding a key. On the floor he would place an upside-down plate. Once he fell into a deep sleep, he would drop the key onto the plate and the noise would wake him. He would be energized, renewed, and ready to reapply himself to his work.

When confronted with solving a problem in your inventive effort, try sleeping for a short while, then wake and write down the images you can recall from your subconscious dreams. Before nodding away, ask your creative mind for an answer to the problem you are working on and then enjoy a short break.

## Happenstance Observations

> happenstance: a circumstance especially that is due to chance
>
> –*Merriam-Webster*

In these circumstances things just happen that are not intended to happen and can reveal the missing components to the invention you are seeking. It's important to keep your sense of observation alert to unusual events and to question their possibilities in your work at inventing.

Scottish doctor and scientist Alexander Fleming was searching for antibacterial medicines while studying wound infections during World War I. His first discovery was lysozyme, an enzyme that had weak antibacterial properties. This discovery met with limited success, but he continued his research.

Fleming was notoriously untidy. While conducting a series of experiments in 1928 involving the staphylococcal bacteria, he made a mistake that led to a major breakthrough in medicine. Leaving for a monthlong vacation, he stacked all his cultures of staphylococci bacteria on a bench in the corner of his lab. When he returned on September 3, 1928, he noticed one of the petri dishes sitting near an open window was left uncovered. This one petri dish had become contaminated with mold spores. Fleming observed that the bacterium adjacent to the mold was dying. He then isolated the mold and studied its properties, identifying a liquid that the mold had produced as the antibacterial agent. The liquid evolved into penicillin, the world's first antibiotic.

When you are fully engaged in your pursuit of a solution, circumstances may present something that you observe consciously and this observation reveals an answer that you are seeking, like my experience with a cast-iron kettle (story to follow below) or even my experience with the book in the bookstore presented in the introduction; if you are asking yourself questions about what might be a solution, one will often appear—the creative mind works in mysterious ways.

As you work on solving your inventive problem with a unique invention and continue to message your creative mind requesting help and input, just be alert to everything that might be a connection to finding your solution. Stimulate responses from your creative mind with the exercises of idea creation from the previous chapter and watch for messages that may reveal the answers you are asking for.

## THE KERNEL OF INVENTION

### • Alexander Graham Bell (1847-1922) •

*"I cannot overestimate the importance of observing every little thing and of reasoning upon it. The history of invention is full of incidents in which apparently trivial observations have proved of immense value to the world."* –Alexander Graham Bell

**Alexander Graham Bell was to follow in the footsteps of his father and grandfather, teaching the deaf to communicate. His father had a substantial following in England. However, the Bell family lost two sons to the "white plague" (tuberculosis) that was prevalent in densely populated London. Alexander had spells of poor health, and his father, Alexander Melville Bell, made a bold**

decision to move the family to Canada to restore and preserve their health. Alec was 23 at this point and was not at all pleased with this turn of events. During the voyage, he kept to himself and read a new book he bought in London written by German scientist Hermann von Helmholtz, which would turn out to be a fateful decision for Bell. The book was *On the Sensations of Tone*.

The telegraph had fascinated Bell from his first exposure, and he had conducted some very primitive experiments building and testing telegraph models, duplicating commercial process, while still living in England. Upon the move to Canada, Bell was no longer working and was recovering from his bout of poor health. With time on his hands, he set out to further study telegraphy and to learn its scientific intricacies. He set up a small lab and became obsessed with the thought of solving the problem of sending multiple messages over one wire via telegraph. The existing process of telegraph messaging required that one message at a time be sent over any wire, in one direction. This was such a financial restriction on telegraph operations that a method to send multiple messages was thought to be the holy grail of communication (and worth a fortune to whoever solved it).

Helmholtz in his book on tone had described his experiments to synthesize vowel sounds by tuning forks using sound vibrations; Bell felt that by combining Helmholtz's theories of tone vibration and the electrical impulses from telegraph functions he could create a harmonic telegraph that could carry multiple messages at one time.

With the help of his father, Alec received an offer to teach at the recently established Boston School for Deaf Mutes run by Miss Sarah Fuller. Bored with life in the countryside of Canada, Alexander couldn't wait to be on his way south to Boston. He soon was immersed in his new career and his talents were quickly recognized within the teaching community.

Alec was thrilled to earn a living and live on his own in an

*continued*

exciting, thriving city filled with opportunity; he started his own school, providing speech lessons to supplement his teaching.

He never forgot about his telegraph experiments of a few years earlier in England and those in Canada, and when he recognized that the telegraph talent of the day congregated in the Boston area, he returned to working on his dream of providing a harmonic telegraph. He visited the newly formed Massachusetts Institute of Technology (MIT) to see an exhibit of Helmholtz's experiments with tuning forks and sounds by vibration, only to discover that he misunderstood what he had read on the ship's voyage (the book was in German). He thought he read that vowel sounds had been duplicated by vibration and sent over an electric wire to another location, but the scientist had only duplicated the vowel sounds on tuning forks. This misunderstanding became Bell's obsession and the foundation of his belief that human sound could be sent over electric wires (his hypothesis). He renewed his experimentation immediately with the determination to create a harmonic telegraph that could carry multiple messages at one time. After teaching and tutoring day and evening, he would experiment with his dream deep into the night.

Edison and other inventors were pursuing the solution to multiple messages on a single line following an electrical theory path, incorporating modifications to components and currents to find the eventual solution. Bell was hampered because he had less electrical knowledge and understanding; he had to teach himself as he went. But Bell knew speech and sound and sought a solution based on these principles. Bell asked a doctor friend for help acquiring a human ear, which he used as an experiment to study the replication of hearing sound. He observed how the compression of air and the vibrations of sound affected the bones of the ear. In one experiment, Bell attached a small writing instrument to an ear bone in order to draw lines on smoked glass when reacting to sound.

After much observation and study, Bell removed himself to a private location that he called his "dreaming place." It was located on a bluff in Canada, overlooking the Grand River. He had a wicker chair hidden in a secluded spot where a tree had blown over, creating a space nearly invisible to others. In this spot, free from distractions, he could communicate with his creative mind, and he visualized what he knew from his experiments and studies on sound and vibrations; he reflected on everything he had done toward his inventive goal. He hypothesized that sound waves travel through air in the same way that energy moves the coils of a spring when a section of the spring is compressed and released; it was this process that led him to his key theory that electric currents could mimic a pattern of compression and release (rarefactions), which then could duplicate sound. In his secluded space, looking off into the sky, away from his experiments and visualizing in his mind's eye what he knew and had learned, his breakthrough moment occurred. Once recognized, he knew he would eventually solve the problem.

From Bell we learn that:

- Different knowledge from unrelated fields can lead to breakthrough inventions.
- Following a single desire toward an inventive solution will eventually lead to a breakthrough.
- Often a mistake or misunderstanding can be a key to your direction.
- After a period of fully involved study and experimentation toward an inventive breakthrough, retiring to a private place and visualizing and reflecting on what you know can engage the subconscious mind to communicate solutions.
- The applied use of your creative mind in ways we discuss in this book will deliver results.

SOURCES: Charlotte Gray's biography *Reluctant Genius*; *Alexander Graham Bell* by Jennifer Groundwater; internet references; and the Alexander Graham Bell National Historic Site in Baddeck, Nova Scotia.

• PART •

# INVENTIVE STEPS

• CHAPTER 9 •

# Evolving Ideas into Inventive Solutions

**STEP 10:** Form testable theories and evaluate the results.

**STEP 11:** Enhance value and distinguish unique properties.

**THE PROBLEM WITH** ideas is that many would-be inventors think the idea is the solution. When they have what they believe is a good idea to solve their inventive problem, they stop their effort and look for success. An idea isn't an invention; it can't be patented and no one will buy it. Ideas have no value in and of themselves. Ideas are powerful, motivating, and necessary, but they are the kernels to be planted, nourished, and cared for until they blossom into fully developed concepts, proven theories, and manifestations of the idea that can function and perform to solve your inventive problem in a unique way.

Congratulations, you have your ideas. Now let's work with them. We will discuss proven methods to test, expand, and enhance your chosen ideas. The first step is to develop theories based on your ideas that can be tested to prove your idea solution, similar to how scientists solve their chosen problems.

The second step is to enhance the properties of your solution by applying methods to make your idea more valuable and to ensure its uniqueness in order to protect your inventions with intellectual property.

Your ideas must be tested to prove they are effective in solving your problem; they must be functional, practical, and dependable. If you have a number of ideas for your solution, it is just too overwhelming and time-consuming to build physical prototypes of all your ideas. Forming and testing your ideas as theories can substitute for physical prototyping.

## CONVERTING IDEAS INTO TESTABLE THEORIES

By now you've likely determined your favorite ideas, so start with these. Experimentation and testing your assumptions will help you determine next steps based on your experiments' successes and failures.

In forming theories, you are looking to disprove some ideas as well as prove them as a method to narrow your choices. As our famous consulting detective Sherlock Holmes often said, "When you have eliminated the impossible, whatever remains, however improbable, must be the truth."

### Creating Theories by Deduction

Deductions use the known to predict the unknown. As you gather information and facts related to your solution and the ideas you have generated, you can apply this process of reasoning, forming known statements from which conclusions are drawn. What can you expect to be true from the research that you have gathered, as it pertains to each idea for an inventive solution?

Holmes would use his observations and known facts of a case to deduce a total chain of events in a crime, sometimes based on a single observation. In "The Five Orange Pips," he compared this process to how the French anatomist George Cuvier was able to describe an entire animal by analyzing a single bone. From there he had to test and prove enough of his deductions to show they were correct or modify a deduction if it proved incorrect.

What you can reasonably assume from your sets of facts forms a deduction: you are drawing an assumed conclusion. It is a method of reasoning to draw a conclusion that will be correct if all your assumptions leading up to it are correct. If any aren't correct, you will find out by testing your deduction. If one or more premise is wrong, then you can change it and form a new deduction.

When we were creating a recirculating vent for cooking appliances, I deduced that if I had a vacuum force attachment mounted over the top of an oven that was activated when the door opened, I could capture the discharge air and moisture that was released into the room. My known facts were (1) the air that needed to be captured and cleaned was emitted to the room when the door was opened; (2) there was less need for venting when the door was closed; and (3) the emissions are hot, so they will exit upward. My unknown that needed proving was (4) suction will pull an airstream, heat, and moisture into a capture vessel if it is powerful enough. We created the theories on paper and in sketches, then looked for an easy way to quickly prove or disprove what we deduced.

I was wrong—the heat rising and the velocity of the air emitted from an open door were too powerful to capture with an instantaneous vacuum. My unknown was wrong, but it led me to study air-capture techniques, and after making several modifications to the theory, it eventually worked perfectly (see photos of testing and final product on page 161.)

In practice, lay out all your facts and observations related to your concept. Then assume results that you will achieve with your testing. Write out your premises and assumed results and then create an outline of how to test each premise to observe the results. Make modifications to your assumptions if something doesn't work as planned.

## Hypothesize

Unlike deduction, hypothesizing starts with assumptions and not known facts. The basis of hypothesizing is forming unproven assumptions that you can test to provide a base for further experimentation. Scientists working with hypotheses will look for patterns in their experimentation and testing of assumptions to then create deductions. Once a pattern is found, the scientist will propose a possible explanation in the form of a hypothesis. In science, the successful conclusion becomes a theory that can be tested and proven and repeated by others. In inventing, you can use this process to create and test methods of causing functions to happen that are a required component of your invention.

Darwin's hypothesis was that life evolved instead of being created, an unknown that needed proving, which once proven became the theory of evolution by natural selection. That the earth is round not flat and that the earth revolves around the sun were both ancient hypotheses that had to be proven to overcome the common belief.

For the purpose of inventing, the hypothesis method can be used to guide you into and through meaningful experimentation to your ultimate objective. As an example, I will return to my sink water heater. In working with the facts of known water heaters and so-called instantaneous water heaters, plus the natural properties of water, I drew conclusions that existing technology was too bulky and inefficient and that ordinary electric resistance heaters were not fast enough to heat water in flow to accomplish what I envisioned. I hypothesized that water could be heated instantaneously in flow if each molecule could be heated volumetrically at the same time. It was a fact that this could not be done by a transfer of heat such as by resistance heaters because first they heat their element, then their sheathing, then the water. It could not be accomplished by heat exchange means because again an exchange medium would need to be heated, which would heat the carrier tube or vessel first, then the water. Both methods would be too slow. I hypothesized that water molecules would heat uniformly and volumetrically if I could convert electrical energy to heat directly and instantly in the water molecules. My job then was to test ways to apply electrical energy to water in flow. My first attempts failed due to shorting of circuits, uncontrolled heating ending with blown fuses, and one small fire. With each failure, I was a step closer to finding a way to accomplish the inventive direction.

My revised hypothesis was that if I could get the sink water to flow through a field of electrically charged particles, the conductivity of the water would cause the water molecules to become electrically charged and the resistance from dissolved solids in the water would cause the water to essentially heat itself almost instantly, converting electrical energy to heat as it flowed through the heat chamber without the problems encountered in the earlier hypothesis. We had to create an electrical circuit that included the water as part of the circuit. This hypothesis became the outline for what we had to build and test to see if it was true.

## Analogy

In this process, you are looking to compare items that are alike in one or multiple ways so that you can form a hypothesis that you can test. What can you compare your idea to? Does this give you fresh ideas for combining into your solution ideas? Does the analogy help you form a new hypothesis to test for success? If your problem has a particular attribute that you are trying to accomplish, what else has that attribute? What has the opposite? If you come up with a category or characteristic you are trying to incorporate into your invention, you can research all types of data in other fields or information sources to create analogies that can provide answers for your development process. Defining an analogy allows you to search for solutions in other fields that might be applied to the solution you are seeking.

What I consider the best analogy epiphany story is that of Philo T. Farnsworth, as told by Evan Schwartz in *The Last Lone Inventor.* Philo was fascinated with the developing field of electronics. From nearly the time he could first read, he daydreamed of solutions to electronic problems, reading about them in *Science & Invention* magazines whenever he had spare time. He would often go into a trance as he performed chores around the family potato farm, daydreaming of electronic concepts. Philo had been reading about the theoretical state of the art in television developed by Paul Nipkow, a Russian inventor working in Germany. Nipkow scanned images by reflecting light off objects, then passing the light through a spinning black disk with small holes. As the wheel spun, it would mechanically scan the image, converting the light from the holes into electrical images that could be transmitted by wire to another spinning disc and be transformed back into the original image and projected onto a screen. It was breakthrough science. Philo was a child of only 14 (almost 15) at this time and only self-schooled from his magazines, but he felt this would never work. There had to be a better way. He read about electron tube experiments by Karl Braun; Braun was experimenting in transporting electron beams inside vacuum tubes from one part, the cathode, to a fluorescent screen in another part of the tube, causing the screen to light up. Philo thought of these things early on a summer morning in 1921 as he mounted a single-disc harrow pulled by two horses and headed for the field to cultivate the potatoes. His head was filled with thoughts of electronics and the things he had learned from his readings, wondering about electron beams and capturing images electronically. He fell into his normal thought trance as he worked. At one point, he gazed back on the row upon row of furrows he had plowed and inspiration struck him with such force that he froze and nearly fell. He realized that just as a field needed to be plowed row by row, light had to be captured line by line and converted into electrical current and re-created in a similar fashion. This formed his hypotheses and began his lifetime pursuit of inventing and improving television. The analogy of rows of turned earth gave Philo the secret to modern television.

Another favorite story of drawing an analogy to find a solution occurred in 1977. A couple of women were commiserating about their pains from running exercises. There weren't any bras designed for adequate support over miles of bouncing. One commented that men had their jockstraps but women didn't. In that analogy lay the solution and their future. This analogy sent the women into prototyping. They cut up jockstraps and sewed them back together and created the first sports bra, which they then called a JogbraJockbra (later renamed the Jogbra).

They formed a company with a $5,000 loan, ran the business for about a dozen years, and sold the business to Playtex, becoming quite wealthy. Original Jogbras are now in the Smithsonian Museum and the Metropolitan Museum of Art. The Jogbra at the time of the sale exceeded $800 million a year as a clothing category; today it's over a $7 billion industry worldwide.

What can you draw an analogy from that relates to your particular problem? Where does it lead you? Just ask yourself these questions and stay alert for possibilities. When you have one, convert it into a testable deduction or hypothesis and begin testing.

You will use one or more of these techniques to develop test criteria for your inventive ideas. It may require multiple tries, but in this way, you will evolve your original ideas into proven concepts. Then your job is to design the result into functional products or systems.

At the point when you have completed your theory evaluations, it is time to choose one solution to take into further development. The following methods will help you define attributes and unique properties to include in your invention design.

## ENHANCE YOUR INVENTION'S UNIQUENESS

The methods described in the following section have been used by inventors for centuries and can guide you in finalizing your inventions, determining how your embodiment should look, what it should be composed of, and how it should function. The techniques mostly use existing knowledge to give your new creation form and shape and most importantly nonobvious uniqueness.

### The Method of Combining

While testifying in an infringement suit brought against him, Henry Ford stated, "I invented nothing new. I simply assembled into a car the discoveries of other men behind whom were centuries of work."

One definition of inventing is combining what exists in new ways to create new uses or usefulness that haven't been previously recognized.

There are new discoveries and new theories generated every day, but inventions usually have a basis in something that already exists. You have your solution idea and are now beginning to design the finished invention.

The form, function, and attributes will likely be combinations of known science or known attributes of existing things, combined in a unique and new way to achieve particular results. James Webb Young in his book *A Technique for Producing Ideas* describes ideas as "a new combination of old elements." Ask yourself what existing things can be combined to create a new function or result that can give you a piece to your invention's final form. When you see something that might serve a purpose toward your solution but it isn't quite right, ask what can be removed and replaced with something else that will get the necessary job done. A combining of existing properties generally leads to new possibilities. Examine pieces of information related to your problem and think about what exists that might be combined to achieve new results in your invention.

Johannes Gutenberg, a 15th-century metallurgist was seeking a new way to mass-produce the Bible (his problem statement). Monks at the time used handcrafted wooden plates for each page. A piece of his solution came to him upon observing the use of stamps to seal letters with wax, leaving an imprint of the seal in the wax. He envisioned lining up individual stamps with letters to form words, sentences, and paragraphs. This piece of his solution stayed with him but the remainder of the solution eluded him. One day he attended a wine festival and saw wine merchants pressing grapes with hand-cranked presses. Gutenberg's imagination combined the letters and the wine press, and his moveable type printing press solution was born.

To find combinations, search for relationships in the facts and research you have done. When you look with the purpose of finding new combinations in mind, more possibilities become apparent. Write yourself a note (where are the relationships?) and post it where you can see it when looking at your research material. Gutenberg saw a relationship between the mechanism that pressed grapes and inserted the idea of pressing letter stamps (type) onto parchment.

What is the appeal of the solution to your particular problem? What would make it more appealing or better functioning? Look for something that exists that you can combine with one of your ideas to make it better. Start with your own list of ideas. If you have solicited ideas from others, what idea of someone else's can you combine with yours to provide a better design solution? From your research, especially prior art patents, what might work in conjunction with one of your ideas to provide a better solution? Look at other fields, magazines, images, and research papers in related and nonrelated fields. What can you pick out that could combine into an idea you have toward determining your solution's embodiment or design?

What is the purpose of your solution? What purpose is like your purpose but for a different reason? Look there for design solutions. In one instance, we were inventing a new type of clothing steamer and had to enclose the garments in a bag that was free standing. We found our solution when we hit upon studying tent designs; the designs of tents that assembled quickly with flexible tubing and shock cords. This provided the inspiration for our final design solution (see drawings below).

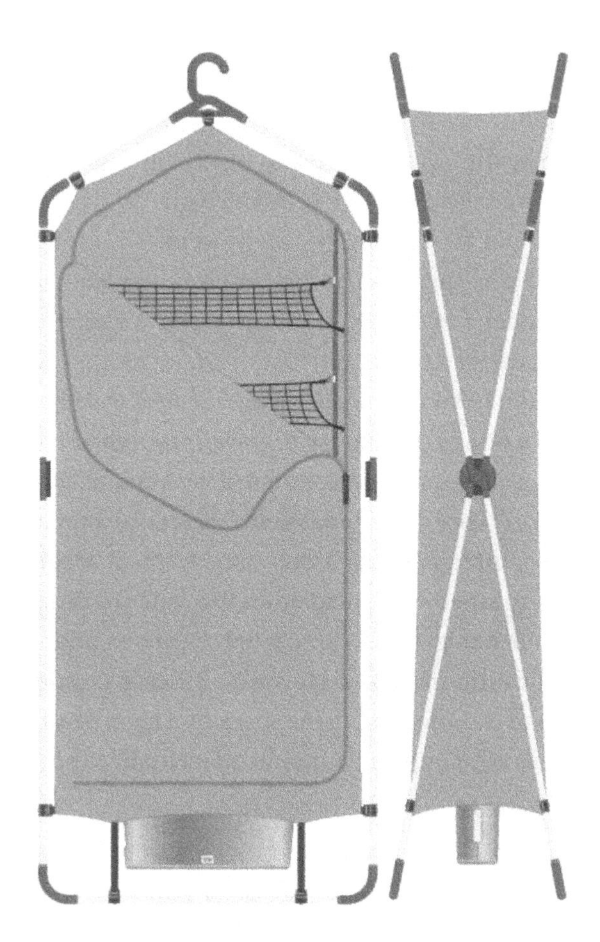

## The Method of Borrowing

Ralph Waldo Emerson wrote, "An inventor knows how to borrow, and everyone is, or should be, an inventor."

Borrowing is a form of combining: taking complete systems, components, or designs from entirely different fields or the work of others, and combining them to your field of inventive endeavor to create something new.

One method is borrowing from expired patents. The patent system was created to share technology. The patent process grants a monopoly to an inventor for a limited time in exchange for complete details of how to build and use what was invented. Once the patent expires anyone can use what it conveys.

You can use ideas, designs, and details you find in expired patents for your final design solution and details from existing patents that are not part of claims.

You can borrow from nature. Swiss electrical engineer George de Mestral discovered the principles of Velcro while hunting with his dog. Mestral's pants and his dog's fur became covered with cockleburs. Mestral wondered how they attached themselves and later studied their construction under a microscope. His invention is a near exact adaptation of nature's design.

What is similar to your problem? What is the opposite of your problem? What have others done to try to solve this problem or a problem like it, or its opposite problem? Are there ideas you can adapt into your problem solution? Look at different fields for similar problems or solutions. Look at nature: many solutions come from an adaptation of nature. Is there any aspect of your solution that you can draw an analogy to in nature, which might then be adapted to your solution?

According to author Michael Michalko, Thomas Edison said that it was important to pay attention to the successful ideas of others because "your idea needs to be original only in its adaptation to the problem you are working on."

## The Method of Reapplication

Reapplication is when you take something old and make it new again by applying it in a new way.

From my own experience, my creative mind led me to take something old and apply it in a new way while working on my food steamer invention. I had spent a couple of years working on improving commercial food steamers for large-scale cooking applications. Food steamers have been a part of the food-service industry for a century and are still a staple of commercial cooking. However, they presented numerous problems or nuisances to operators, and the food results also needed improvement. We had a design coming together, but it lacked the inventive uniqueness I was seeking to ensure patentability.

At one point during the process, I had the opportunity to visit Deer Valley in Park City, Utah, to ski with a friend. On my final afternoon there, I strolled down historic Main Street browsing all the shops. Well hidden in the back corner of an antique shop, all rusty and covered with cobwebs, sat an old cast-iron Dutch oven kettle, the type with a turned-up lip on the lid and legs on the bottom. I might have walked right by without seeing it, but I had to stop to tie my shoe at that time and saw the kettle between shelves. It hit me right there! I drew an analogy between the cooking chamber of our design and the Dutch oven. I needed to reapply the design of a Dutch kettle into our new steamer. Going way back to wagon train days, Dutch ovens were the primary cooking vessel because of their versatility. The proper-use method is to have a charcoal or wood fire below the kettle and to shovel coals to the raised lip on the lid so that the kettle conducts heat to all surfaces and radiates gentle heat to surround the food. The results are tender, juicy, tasty food. We built a Dutch oven cast-metal chamber to fit in a stainless-steel cabinet, heating the top, bottom, and side surfaces. Steam was generated in the bottom of the steamer surrounding the food with a gentle cooking heat. Our steamer top heat controlled the condensing of steam because of the conducting metal remaining hotter than the steam on the surface above the food, which kept excess moisture from falling into the cooking pans, thus improving the quality of the food. We were awarded US Patent 6,310,325 for the controlled condensing of steam in a cooking appliance. That heavy kettle rode on my lap as I flew back to Vermont and is still used in my backyard cooking , and our commercial steam-cooking appliances are still serving the food-service industry today. Our steamer was a reapplication of Dutch oven cooking.

## The Method of Exaggeration

What if your solution went way beyond its original purpose? How big of a solution could that be? Could it take on national or international proportions? Regarding my sink booster heater, instead of heating water at the sink, how about heating liquid food or pasteurizing milk or reducing maple sap to syrup or purifying contaminated water or desalinating salt water? What would it take? How would you do it? What would happen? The idea here is to think of magnifications of your solution, much bigger applications or uses, and then work backward toward your eventual invention. Have you solved a much bigger problem than you intended, making your work far more valuable?

## The Method of Modification

In some cases, you can enhance your solution and its uniqueness by eliminating or modifying it in some fashion. What can you change about your potential solution or your problem (or an idea you are looking to combine or borrow) to generate new ideas? What other uses might it serve? Can you eliminate some aspect or do it in an entirely different way? Can you add something to create a new result and added benefit?

Adaptive methods can help you finalize your inventive idea, help define the component parts and functions needed to support your solution, and help you establish the embodiment your invention will take.

To the clothing steamer mentioned earlier, I decided to add an atomizer to provide a freshening ingredient to the clothing using modification to make the problem solution more unique.

Use whatever techniques are right for your particular idea solution. The objective is to improve what you will achieve with your solution, making it more valuable and distinguishing it sufficiently to secure intellectual property, both enhancing your solution and its value.

## THE KERNEL OF INVENTION

### • Dr. John Gorrie (1803-1855) •

The first verifiable history of Dr. John Gorrie is that in 1824 he worked in the apothecary owned by Dr. Samuel Green in Columbia, South Carolina. Gorrie's first medical training was the preparation of treatments from recipes found in the *Edinburgh Pharmacopeia.* In addition to grinding, weighing, mixing botanicals, dispensing pills and powders, attending to customers, and keeping the record books as assistant to Dr. Green, Gorrie assisted in patient care, performing unskilled and semi-skilled procedures as he was called upon. Gorrie acquired a varied knowledge of the medical beliefs of the time.

It was during this apprenticeship that Gorrie encountered the effects of the deadly fevers that haunted the area in the summertime. When the fever hit Columbia, signs of death were evident everywhere. He observed the wagons as they hauled bodies to the cemetery and warnings posted throughout the city to avoid areas where illness existed for fear of becoming contaminated. The air itself seemed to reek of death. Despite the best efforts of the established medical community, the epidemics went mostly unchecked until they retreated on their own for another year when colder weather set in.

The effect this had on Gorrie was a dedication to medicine and a goal of eliminating the pain and suffering he observed by finding treatments and perhaps a cure for the fevers.

He chose to study medicine at the College of Physicians and Surgeons of the Western District of New York (also known as

*continued*

the Fairfield Medical School). He completed his required lecture studies early, in his second year, qualifying him to study under an established doctor for three years and to complete his essay on a chosen subject. He returned to the Carolinas to complete his preparation.

In 1833, Gorrie traveled by a riverboat to the isolated, lawless town of Apalachicola, Florida. Apalachicola was in its early formative years, located on a delta of the Apalachicola River and the Gulf of Mexico, and was ideally suited as a port town for the developing cotton trade from the plantations of Georgia and Alabama. It promised opportunity to the bankers, merchants, speculators, and traders that migrated there. It also promised the threat of the fevers that arrived early in the season and lingered until frost in November. Gorrie was welcomed as a truly professional man, a genuine doctor, and most importantly a man experienced with the fevers.

Gorrie took quarters at a boardinghouse where rivermen and transient workers stayed as well. Often the food was rancid or spoiled due to the lack of ice, which had to be shipped from Lake Erie. But it was a frontier town in its early stages and there weren't a lot of choices.

Gorrie made the acquaintance of Dr. William D. Price, already established with a practice in Apalachicola. Since he made so little money doctoring, Price also served as the postmaster, a bank appraiser, and a customs inspector. Price greatly feared the fever that prevailed five months a year and saw the opportunity to pass responsibilities to Gorrie, so he could pack up and leave during the sickness months (as many others did). Gorrie became apprenticed under Price and also became assistant postmaster and handled most all of the duties charged to Price.

Over the next few years, Gorrie became entrenched in the activities of Apalachicola and its growth and development. His big worry was still the sickness that invaded the territory when the weather turned warm. For some time, Gorrie had been petitioning for improvements to sanitary conditions, arguing that standing pools of water, raw sewage dumped on streets and into streams, and trash and garbage dumped in the river contributed to the disease now known as malaria. The onset of warm weather was definitely a contributing factor. Gorrie began to ask himself if he had the ability to alleviate this curse. He reasoned that the spread of the sickness was airborne and was aided by warmth and moisture.

He drew an analogy to the cold that the northern climates suffered in the winter. If homes in the north were built to keep out the cold, couldn't homes in the hot areas be built to keep out the heat and to remove the moisture from the air? He deduced that this would help prevent people from becoming infected with the dreaded disease.

It was a time of tight money in the region and his receipts from patients and from his various appointments decreased considerably. Gorrie chose to spend more and more time with his problem project than political or business interests. He set his sights on devising some practical way to condition living spaces to be safer and more livable in the hot months.

Year after year, Gorrie had observed firsthand the results of the fever (malaria) and treated its victims. He continued to preach for more sanitary conditions and believed the stagnant water and heat related to the seasons contributed to this curse. In 1849, a greater epidemic hit: yellow fever. It had been a mild winter without hard frosts and an early spring with hotter weather. When the epidemic started in early May, there was little to do except tend the sick and try to contain the spread. Every day new victims died and new cases were reported in the region. Gorrie spent day and night attending the sick. Through experimentation, he discovered some helpful aids and treatments that saved a few lives, but he was on the verge of exhaustion and refused to rest.

In the waning days of September, the weather quickly shifted; the townspeople called it hurricane days. Gorrie was

*continued*

attending a fever patient who was delirious. As the weather quickly removed the oppressive heat and wind rose and rain began to fall, Gorrie experienced exhilaration he had not felt for months. His body seemed lighter and his tension loosened; he was free of the weight of the heat. Upon checking his patient, her breathing had become normal, she slept peacefully, and most remarkably she no longer had a fever. It was the moment when Gorrie was fully committed to the belief that *cold* was the healer, the cure for the fevers; he prayed for an early winter. During late October, his prayers were answered when clear cold nights set in for the season. The epidemic disappeared.

The records are unclear, but it seems Dr. Gorrie may have received a small inheritance about this time, and began making annual trips to New York where he could avail himself of talent and instruments to assist in the prototyping of his model to test his theory that cold could successfully treat the fevers. He reasoned that ice "had a vitalizing effect upon the body and would aid in resisting the causes of malarial diseases." He initiated a study of the many ways in which artificial cold could be produced. He settled on what he considered the most practical. Dr. William Cullen, a Scottish physician, presented a theory in an essay called "Cold Produced by Evaporative Fluids." Cullen's theory proposed a pump in a closed vessel of water could reduce the atmospheric pressure, causing the water to freeze.

Gorrie conducted a great deal of experimentation on compressing air and eventually arrived at a design he considered ideal for his purposes. It involved a pump with a cylinder, four inches in diameter, and a piston with a two foot stroke capable of thirty strokes per minute. His tests and calculations showed that such an instrument could produce 22 cubic feet of cold air per hour, or 500 cubic yards per day, adequate to cool most homes of the day. Challenges remained, however: How do you practically power the chilling device? And ideally the chilled air must be dry to aid in the healthful advantages. He found the drying answer in existing physics: by condensing the air into reduced spaces, it gave up its ability to retain moisture proportionately. He began applying his theory and prototype discoveries into building a "fever room" in a bedroom below his office.

He determined that he must find a way to circulate purified air and devised a means by which a container of ice would be suspended from the ceiling of the fever room and a hole cut in the floor above the vessel. The hotter air would vent through the hole into the chimney (where Gorrie relied on the carbon to clean and purify the air). Colder air, chilled by the ice, would fall due to its higher specific gravity. A third pipe with a valve allowed for circulation of open air completing a cycle of ventilation.

The problem with the system was that it needed a supply of ice, which was not readily available, especially in the hot months. For his experiments, Gorrie had hoarded enough ice from ship deliveries in the cooler months and had large blocks buried ten feet deep between layers of sawdust in the ground of his yard. He knew he must find a mechanical way to produce ice to ensure the success of his chilling and healing system. He returned to his earlier studies of chilling water, intent on inventing a machine to make ice.

He succeeded in having a prototype built and received a London patent in 1850 and a US patent in 1851.

In late June 1850, Dr. Gorrie confided in a friend that he had succeeded in manufacturing ice and shared the product with him, asking only to keep it a secret until he was ready.

For the sake of improving the health of the masses, Dr. Gorrie sacrificed much of his career and money. But the revealing of his true invention, the ice maker, was conducted in a more frivolous way. A popular French consul, returning favors to his friends and colleagues in Apalachicola, planned a grand celebration for Bastille Day and promised the most elaborate dinner the town had ever seen. Except it was mid-July and there was no ice to chill the wines. "Only a miracle" could save the

*continued*

feast, he confided to his friend Dr. Gorrie, who immediately promised to deliver a miracle. The consul enjoyed his gambling and began taking bets before the grand event that on Bastille Day he would have ice to cool the wines. The locals knew that no delivery was possible at that time of year and gladly took the wager. When the time came, the serving room doors swung open and waiters appeared, carrying large silver trays covered with blocks of ice and copious amounts of champagne. Gorrie revealed how he had made a device to manufacture ice and Monsieur Rosan, the consul, went about the room collecting on his wagers.

In inventing the ice machine and room-chilling techniques, Dr. Gorrie felt his work would improve medical treatment and minimize the fevers. Through years of observation and hunch assessments as to causes, Dr. Gorrie failed to identify the real cause of malaria and yellow fever, and his cure inventions failed to adequately treat the sick and dying. Instead he invented air-conditioning and the ice maker, both of which serve us as major inventions to this day. He did advance the understanding of the diseases and on more than one occasion came close to identifying the cause, but the common knowledge that the diseases traveled in the vapors of the air blocked the observation that mosquitos also thrived in the same conditions identified with the outbreaks of the dreaded diseases.

There are inventive lessons in this story, but Dr. Gorrie failed to benefit financially from his successes and never realized the medical benefits he sought. His backer, whom he had granted 75 percent ownership in his patents, died unexpectedly and left no provision for continued support. The public and commercial enterprise failed to adapt a support for "artificial ice" and his patent for conditioning air failed to issue. A few years after Gorrie's death, Ferdinand Carré released a commercially successful ice machine based upon the principles of Gorrie's invention.

We learn from Dr. Gorrie:

- Altruism is one motivation to invention.
- Early base knowledge is essential to understanding and invention, but basing your work on one premise that is wrong and never questioning this base premise can lead to failure at achieving your inventive goal. The underlying cause of the diseases was not questioned.
- Sometimes you create a meaningful invention for humanity that others derive the financial benefit from. Plan for the commercialization of your invention.
- The contributions we make as inventors may be great or small, but for every new discovery and the innovation it brings, we aid the future of our families, our countries, and ourselves, so let's get started today. We don't know how great some of our ideas can be until we do something with them.

SOURCES: The John Gorrie Museum in Apalachicola, Florida; the out-of-print book *The Fever Man* by V. M. Sherlock; and internet references.

• CHAPTER 10 •

# Assessment and Preparing for Market Success

**STEP 12:** Evaluate acceptance of your inventive solution.

**STEP 13:** Assess the industry and companies your solution addresses.

**ASSESSING OUR OWN** work isn't easy because we fall in love with our own ideas and creations. Up to this point, you've invested time and energy and perhaps some money into what you have determined to be a worthy problem requiring an inventive solution, into evaluating ideas for solution development, and into steps leading up to commercialization on one type or another. Your next steps will involve investing in prototypes of your solution, protecting your inventive concepts with patents, and either negotiating licensing deals or entering a business to manufacture a product or deliver a service. You will in all likelihood spend a great deal of money and additional time adequately executing this stage. Many inventors need financial help at this stage either through investors, a sponsor, loans, or grants of some sort. Any third party you approach to assist will require detailed assessment of your market and industry.

It can be argued that assessment should happen much earlier in the invention creation process than where I am presenting it in this book and I don't disagree. It would be difficult to assess your final inventive solution before this point, but your market and industry assessment may come much earlier. Either way, do your assessments before making expensive investments in your inventive solution.

In reality, assessing your problem, your ideas, and your solution, and the work to physically create and commercialize your invention, are ongoing processes that begin with the very first thought about finding a problem and won't end until you remove yourself from your project in some way. Assessment has been a part of your decision-making along the way. However, the process deserves to be reviewed in depth at stages in your progress in order to avoid costly and time-consuming mistakes.

What is important to assess? Well, everything. I will ask ten questions as a good starting point for your review assessment at this stage. This should stimulate other questions you can add to the list and I will address some critical evaluations later in this chapter.

**ASK YOURSELF**

1. Is your inventive problem real?
2. Is there a market for a solution? (Who wants it?)
3. Is the market large enough to justify the time and expense to create a solution?
4. Are there companies that have competing products? How are they doing? Might they want to license a better solution? Can they prevent your entry into this market in any way?
5. Does your solution have sufficient benefit over prior and competitive solutions?
6. Can you create something with unique properties that is useful, new, and nonobvious in order to add value to your solution with patent protection?
7. What will it cost to produce an inventive solution to your problem? Where will the money come from? Do you need investors? Where will you find them?
8. If you are going to start a business and take your solution to market yourself, a business feasibility study would be useful. How will the product or service be manufactured or created? What will it cost? Who will take it to market?

Is there an established method to market that exists in the field you've chosen (representatives, brokers, distributors)? How do you break into these groups?

9. What are all the barriers to market success? How do you address them? (For example, competitors, regulations, unions, price competition, web sales.)
10. Does your solution have the attributes that the market wants?

You owe it to yourself to conduct a thorough and complete review of your work to date and of the solution you intend to take forward before venturing into the next phase.

Walt Disney was a creative genius, but he fully understood the need for deep evaluation and assessment at every stage of his developments. Disney, who was constantly experimenting with more productive techniques toward creativity, relied on one procedure for his early full-length cartoons *Snow White*, *Pinocchio*, *Bambi*, and *Fantasia*, according to Keith V. Trickey, author of a paper entitled "The Walt Disney Creativity Strategy."

Walt used three rooms for the process of creating these films. The first, Room One, was what we would call the brainstorming or idea room. In this room, there were no rules except that it wasn't the place for criticism or evaluation; this room "is where dreams were dreamed," ideas were bountiful, no restrictions, every crazy idea was welcome. When this process was exhausted, the project and people were moved to Room Two, where the ideas were vetted, coordinated, combined, eliminated, and expanded. This is where Disney's characters and events were sequenced and story boards depicting the ideas were created. Room Three, which they called the sweat box, was a small room under a set of stairs where the entire crew would assemble and critically review the project to date. Every negative was discussed and analyzed. An important aspect of this process is that once the critique stage is entered the group is assessing a combined work, not the work of one individual. From this first critical review, the process returned to Room One and ideas based on the work to date were generated, beginning the cycle again until the project was completed, modified, or abandoned.

Scott Belsky, author of *Making Ideas Happen*, adds that "the idea bloodshed that occurs in Room Three is just as important as the wild ideation of Room One." To properly assess your solution, you need your version of a Room Three.

## INVENTIVE SOLUTION ASSESSMENT

You have been assessing your solution every step of the way. Your views on your idea and solution are not about to change at this point, at least from a self-assessment process. The step here, which ties to market assessment, is to engage others in the assessment process. There are different ways to do this, but again I will stress you need to protect your work by revealing your solution only to people who have signed a confidentiality, nonuse, and nondisclosure agreement.

In my early years of inventing, I tried to ignore my love of my creations and would conduct this reality-check assessment myself. It's not a bad idea if you can be truly objective. I would visit manufacturing and sales organizations involved in the area my problem solution addressed; I would walk trade show floors and without revealing my solution ask "What if there was something that solved the problem of . . . ?" Involving those who sell, distribute, service, or market similar solutions can provide a great deal of product input and market assessment. Check for associations serving your market for names of prominent players in these categories.

My preference at this stage is to have a professional business consultant prepare a product and market review to guide your efforts. Choose one that knows your market and product category. Check their references and get an NDA signed. To find someone, turn to local business lawyers, bankers, patent attorneys, or venture capitalists. Check to see if there is a local angel group (start-up investors) in your region and contact its organizer. All these professions will have contacts with business analysts. The insight and guidance a few thousand dollars can buy will save you many multiples over the next phases of your effort. Even with a professional business consultant there is the possibility that they can misinterpret the value of your invention, so it is prudent for you to hone your presentation to start them off and cover your problem, your solution, its benefits, and its unique aspects. Include what you know about your target market and ask a lot of questions. Before engaging anyone, request a detailed proposal including a description of the deliverables. Make sure to question their qualifications, even when well recommended, and let them sell you on their expertise and approach.

Another source would be the small business association in your state, which may be less costly but may deliver mixed results.

The management of local incubator sites, where new enterprises are born and assistance is provided, is worth exploring. By their nature, these are local organizations where you can receive guidance, advice, and mentorship to start and accelerate a business effort. You can find one in your local area by simply searching online.

You may still want to do the preliminary work yourself. The following market assessment section can help.

## MARKET ASSESSMENT

Market assessment is about knowing who the customers for your inventive solution will be, what their needs are, and why they will choose your solution to meet those needs over what they can get from any competitive source. This doesn't mean there is a competitive product in existence, but it addresses the issue of need fulfillment. A market assessment at this stage is primarily for your purposes, but if done well it will provide the bones of a full-blown market and feasibility study that you will likely need if you seek bank financing, investors, or licensing your invention. The purpose at this stage is broadly evaluating your solution's potential for market success.

In our invention business, we would often conduct this assessment ourselves and then engage professionals to complete the full feasibility study after the product was developed adequately to begin looking at manufacturing or licensing to an established business.

Market success should be focused on the end user and their needs, much like the solution assessment. However, the research usually starts with the industry and the companies making up the industry in which your solution falls.

What do you need to know? Who are the players? Who are their customers? Find trends and forecasts (especially growth trends). Is it a growing or declining industry? What is its size? Is it a national, international, or regional industry? What is the typical way product is sold in the industry? Who among the players has product that would compete with yours, be complementary to yours, or be enhanced by yours?

As you research the industry, compile a list of names to contact by phone to discuss the industry and to ask questions that will give you a greater insight to entering the industry (directly or indirectly). If you intend to license your invention, also compile a list of names at potential target companies and the names of executives engaged in marketing, sales, development, legal, and sometimes engineering.

I do not consider company engineers the place to start; they are often a barrier to introducing your invention because your project might compete for resources with ongoing projects, be deemed a threat, or be looked at as additional unwanted work to do.

A lot of information can be gathered for free on the internet and additional information (potentially a lot of it) can be found at a local library. Libraries subscribe to databases that you cannot access without buying a subscription. A research librarian can be a golden asset in your searches. An additional source is a university or college library. If you are connected or have friends that are connected to these institutions, you can access a tremendous amount of information from their database access; however, if you do not have free access, you will typically be asked to pay a fee. We took an approach of advertising and hiring a part-time researcher from a local university that we engaged at a reasonable hourly rate and assigned research topics. This was a less expensive way to access all the data available at our university and it also produced faster results.

When you initiate an industry and company assessment, begin with studying a general overview of the industry. You can get this from trade journals, websites, and perhaps some web-based analysis from general searches.

To go deeper, find what is termed the industry's NAICS code. This stands for North American Industry Classification System. They publish a wealth of information by standard industry classes. This will make all your research easier and faster and more meaningful. You can access the NAICS and learn how to use it at https://www.census.gov/eos/www/naics/.

Almost every industry has at least one trade association and one or more regularly scheduled trade shows. The executive directors of these associations are typically very accessible and control a vast amount of information that they are willing to share. Often they have reports and studies about their industry for free or at reasonable rates. Over the years many executive directors of trade associations have become my friends and are some of our closest contacts in an industry.

Attending a trade show is a wonderful way to talk to a lot of people associated with an industry. Compile a list of names from manufacturers, customers, trade associations, publications, and informational seminars for future use and keep all the players in one location. If you can, attend an industry trade show as part of your assessment process. A word of caution, though: the companies displaying there are there to talk to customers, so be considerate of their time and attention. The trade show floor is for quick encounters, bits of information, making initial contact for future follow-up, and educational opportunities. If there is competitive product on display, gather information on pricing, even just list pricing. This will help you in running your manufacturing costs and selling prices when you complete development. If you have a contact to introduce you to some key people before a show (trade association directors can help), then you might invite one to a breakfast before the show starts. This makes it comfortable for the contact and doesn't interfere with their work.

From the above research, you will have a list of companies you want to know more about. Web searching is the place to start: visit their website, especially the About Us and Press sections, as well as the section describing their product(s). Search for news or trade articles mentioning the company, look up product names and individual names, and go to LinkedIn to request connections to company employees. If a company is public, you can find a lot more information from sources like Yahoo Finance, Morningstar, the US Securities and Exchange Commission's EDGAR database (https://www.sec.gov/edgar/searchedgar/companysearch.html), and other financial sites.

Depending on your inventive solution industry, there may be other government agencies where you can find a wealth of information. For example, we did a product for medical sanitation monitoring. We spent days studying the information we found at the Centers for Disease Control and Prevention, Centers for Medicare and Medicaid Services, and other health and human resource sites. To work with a list of all government agencies, go to https://www.usa.gov/federal-agencies/a.

A last word, if your assessment requires target market information and demographics: the US Census Bureau can provide the most comprehensive information. Start at https://www.census.gov or an easier data site like American FactFinder at https://factfinder.census.gov/.

When your research is complete, you will have answered all the questions I posed in this chapter and many more that you created in the process of research. You will know more about the product you must create to deliver your inventive solution. You will know details about your intended market and how you will approach it or how you will approach a player in that market. You will know your customers and what will entice them to purchase your product, and you will be well equipped with statistics and numbers to support a compelling case for the future success of your solution. If this is not the case, you must ask yourself if you should move forward with developing this solution or step back to the beginning and reassess your problem—is it the right problem to be solving or should you reevaluate the problem or your solution for a more compelling solution? The ultimate goal is financial success through introducing a new inventive solution or by licensing one to someone that will pay you dearly for the rights. Make sure you are comfortable that your assessments provide you with the confidence of ultimate success and then move forward.

I suggest at this stage that you write a detailed assessment document with relevant facts and statistics from your research and a compelling narrative on the ultimate success of your inventive solution project. This will be needed for any financing or investor solicitation. It would also be used to sell licensing rights to an existing operation to take your solution to market. It will serve as a major portion of a detailed business plan if one becomes required.

## THE KERNEL OF INVENTION

### • Josephine Cochrane (1839-1913) •

Sometimes inventions occur as a result of frustration and necessity. Josephine Garis Cochrane was a socialite in Shelbyville, Illinois, and the wife of a respected businessman who had made a fortune in the dry goods business. Following a dinner party, Cochrane was putting the family's best dishes, handed down for generations, back in the cupboard when she discovered several pieces that had been chipped by the servants while washing. No one hated washing dishes any more than Cochrane, but she ordered that the servants would no longer be allowed to wash the precious wares; she would do it correctly herself. She asked herself, "Why doesn't somebody invent a machine to wash dirty dishes safely?" Then "Why don't I do it myself?" was the quick mental comeback. With this she took herself from the kitchen to her home library, one cup in hand to think it through.

Within a half hour, she had the basis of a working machine based on using water pressure to spray hot soapy water onto dishes held securely in a rack. In her mind, she could see how this machine would work. Although much has changed, it is still the basic concept of dishwashers today, over 130 years later.

In 1883, when Josephine was 45, her husband died, and when the estate was accounted for, Josephine discovered she was broke. She then began her inventive work in earnest, developing a design that could be prototyped. She tested her concept by "throwing" soapy water over plates and saucers in her kitchen. She disregarded her unexpected status of being poor and began setting up shop in the shed behind her house;

*continued*

working with a mechanic named George Butters, she cobbled together a copper boiler, motor, and pump to test her concept as a machine. The first model pumped soapy water onto the surfaces of dishes firmly positioned in carefully measured racks to house different dishes. Within two months, she had a working dishwasher. She received the first of her patents on December 28, 1886. Many more patents were to follow. She formed the Garis-Cochran Company. Sales and profits were a struggle, but she prevailed.

The dishwasher first succeeded in hotels and then hospitals, but the home market was elusive for years. Each installed success such as Boston's Palmer House Hotel and the 1893 World Columbian Exposition in Chicago brought more and more accolades, slowly building the company's reputation. Little money was made until they could move into their own factory in 1898. Josephine died in 1913, still actively growing her company at the age of 74. The company changed names but continued to manufacture machines of Josephine's design and was eventually absorbed into Hobart, a leader in the food equipment marketplace. Hobart eventually released a successful home dishwasher in the late 1940s and named it Kitchen Aid, a brand that is still a leader today as part of the Whirlpool family of appliances.

Josephine faced frustration over chipped china and formulated a solution. Knowing the problem was fairly universal, she invented a design to automate a process while protecting the dishes being treated. And despite her lack of money, she built a business to take care of her and employees and created a lasting and respected brand of equipment.

From Josephine Cochrane we learn:

- Frustration can be the catalyst for invention.
- Sometimes you only need one idea.
- Prototyping is a key part of inventing.
- Building a business around your invention is one method to commercialization.

SOURCES: "The Woman Who Invented the Dishwasher" by J. M. Fenster and internet references.

• PART •

# GETTING PHYSICAL

## Build It, Test It, Break It, Design It

• CHAPTER 11 •

# Physically Developing Your Invention

## Designing, Engineering, and Building Your Prototype

**STEP 14:** Design and build "acts like" (proof of concept) prototype.

**STEP 15:** Design your "looks like" prototype model.

Imagination supplies the ideas; technical knowledge helps carry them out. —Thomas Edison

I hear and I forget, I see and I remember, I do and I understand. —Confucius

**THIS CHAPTER DEALS** with proving your inventive solution and taking steps to turn it into a real product or service ready for your commercialization effort. You may or may not know yet what direction your commercialization will take. You may be entering a business to manufacture or deliver a product, or to execute a new service. You may be heading into an effort to license your invention to another party that will commercialize it and pay you license fees and royalties. We will investigate these options a bit later in the book, but in any case, you need to do a number of things in this phase of your invention creation process in order to make any commercialization effort work.

1. Prove your solution solves the problem you have chosen.
2. Test components and subsystems (assemblies and groupings of components) to perform a function of your invention and assemble subsystems into a working prototype.
3. Design the final embodiment your solution will take and create "looks like" renderings. Finalize a preferred design.
4. Determine the components and materials and estimate the costs of your product in manufactured quantities.

Remember: if your idea doesn't work, it's useless. Since you are dealing with inventive ideas, you must prove to yourself and to everyone else that you have something that solves a problem and something that's unique, nonobvious, and useful (the criteria for issuing a patent). Test every aspect and function of your solution to prove your solution.

## PROTOTYPE TO PROVE YOUR CONCEPT

The purpose of "acts like" prototyping of your product is to prove the concept works and to perfect its functions and ultimately to help add commercial value to the work that you have done. This is not the final design work for your invention; it is the process of determining all the parts and pieces you need to make your invention work and assembling them into a working prototype (all subsystems working together to perform your desired result) to prove that you have a solution to your inventive problem. It does not have to look like your final product—that will come later. I had one "acts like" prototype's subassemblies nailed to a piece of plywood the size of a door, all connected to perform the intended functions (this is called a breadboard). When the embodiment was designed, it was smaller than a breadbox. In the picture on the next page, I show a simple breadboard (the water side; there is also an electronic side) for testing the sink booster heater concept, all constructed of existing components purchased from a supply house.

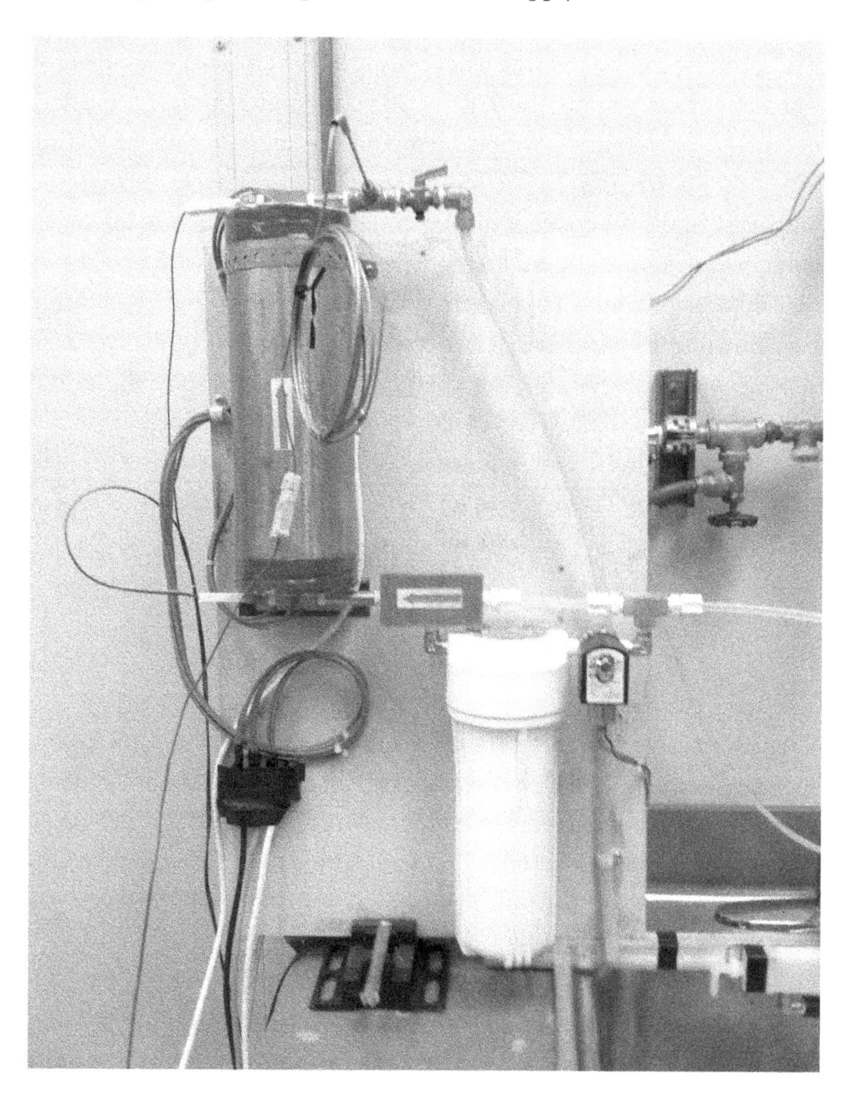

It doesn't matter what early experiments look like or what they are made of; what counts is that you can test a critical piece of your solution before you finalize it. Speedy testing is critical. You can spend way too much time and money trying to design before you realize something has to change. Quickly build experimenting platforms, test right away, and change your tests until you are satisfied.

## DESIGN SPECIFICATION

Start by laying out the known facts and setting the direction for "acts like" prototyping by creating a design specification. This is a guide for you and anyone you may have work on your development. In this document, you summarize the problem and the solution you are taking forward. Summarize the pertinent background research. Provide the pertinent results of concept testing and detail how you anticipate this affecting the design and building phase. In bullet form with any necessary details, provide all specific design requirements and constraints that are known. In some detail, describe the performance that your invention must achieve and how that will be measured. List all desired features. Write out a full description of your vision for a prototype; include sketches or drawings whenever possible. This is also the place to summarize all known design or engineering obstacles to the creation of your solution. Refer to the document periodically as you work.

## "ACTS LIKE" PROTOTYPING

If a picture is worth a thousand words, a prototype is worth a thousand pictures. At Ideas Well Done, we liked to think we said this first, but we didn't, and there are variations of this saying, like IDEO's "A prototype is worth a thousand meetings." I am not sure where the original credit goes, but I do know that prototyping is a creative force. Prototyping is making your inventive solution come to life.

Your objective with "acts like" prototyping is working out all the bugs you'll discover in performance and function before completing a "looks like" design. Prototyping is about finding problems or things that don't work in a physical embodiment of an idea and then changing your process, design, or method to make the problems go away, one at a time.

Early prototyping is building solutions before you know what the final design is. This is part of your design discovery process. Test your solution devices with the simplest simulations you can come up with. In this way, you can prove concepts and, just as importantly, disprove some quickly. Often building what you envision can lead to a greater level of discovery, expanding your solution into a more refined invention. Prototyping doesn't have to be a machine either; you can prototype experiences, business models, and just about any aspect of your inventive developments. Most people think of a prototype as something that looks and operates as it will in the market. Eventually this has to happen. But this is not what you are seeking initially. You want to prototype things to test function and results. Often this can be done with simple and quick processes and materials, depending on the complexity of your invention. With many of the projects we worked on, we used cardboard or poster board, duct tape, scrap metal, and parts and pieces of items we bought and took apart to reassemble into the function we wanted to test. On several occasions, we scoured junkyards to salvage any part that might contribute to our prototyping effort. In the picture below, we are running initial testing on skin sensing for use in our hand sanitation project.

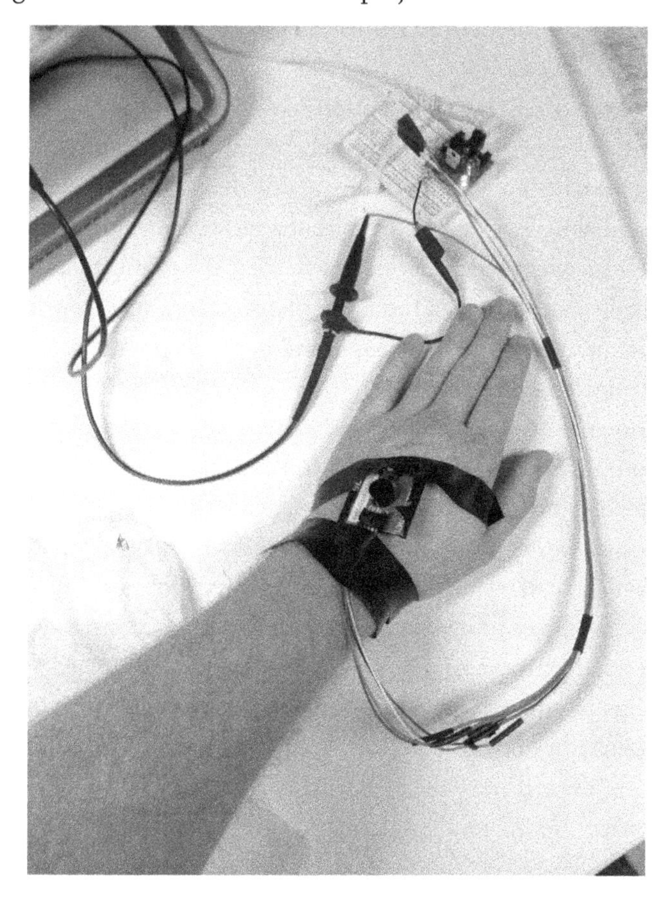

Rapid prototyping (a process of creating testable parts by machines that convert drawings into plastic or metal parts) can play a substantial role in early prototyping of some solutions and the cost has come down dramatically in recent years. Rapid prototyping can provide custom parts for testing before going to the expense of actual manufactured pieces. On one occasion, the shape and feel of a handle was important to our development, so we rapid prototyped a dozen handles to try before deciding on the perfect solution. It was so much easier than assessing the right attributes for the handle using drawings. Rapid prototyping services are available in many communities, and 3-D printers equivalent to those that used to cost several tens of thousands of dollars are now available at office supply chains for hundreds of dollars.

Edison's most common method of inventing involved building something related to his inventive problem in order to test and better understand the problem and the solution he sought. He felt that experimentation was so important that most of his teams were led by the chief experimenter. He would often have other technicians building parts so one experiment could quickly follow the current experiment. This was the case with the lightbulb; at one time, he had several technicians manufacturing glass bulbs so that a new experiment could begin without delay when the prior one failed. He was working on the embodiment at the same time as the inventive solution, to determine bulb shape, filament material and shape, and methods of creating vacuums and bulb electrification.

Experiment and welcome failure. Most inventions take a lot of experimentation. Experiments will fail and you will learn from every failure. It doesn't mean your solution doesn't work; you just haven't perfected the details yet. There are no useless experiments if you observe the results and learn what you can from any failure. Mark Gumz, former CEO at Olympus, said that failure brings understanding and that success is only found by understanding these failures and "acting upon this knowledge."

If you reach a point where progress seems to have stopped or slowed down, focus not on your solution, but on what else you could experiment with, even if it's only randomly connected to your project. See what you can learn and what inspirations might come from these experiments.

## CONCEPT TESTING YOUR EMBODIMENT

### Test Component Parts and Subsystems

One element of your solution will be your invention's components or functional parts purchased from parts manufacturers. You have to determine all the pieces and parts that will comprise your invention. If you are working on a complex problem solution or a solution with multiple functions to support your invention, consider dividing it into a set of subsolutions and process the function of each subsolution on its own. Very often the components that make up these functions already exist and it's a matter of determining what pieces will work together in the right way. As you identify key components, include them in an initial component list.

As one example, with our water booster heater, I isolated it into several subsystems to be dealt with independently. The major subsystem was the water-heating vessel. This became our primary challenge, since we didn't know how we were going to heat the water in flow. Once we had a concept for heating the water almost instantly, we could work on the housing and materials to do the heating. The water plumbing design, the electrical and control components, the temperature controls, and the problem areas like leakage current could be dealt with as separate subsystems. Over 90 percent of the component parts for the booster heater, everything except the heat chamber, already existed but had never been assembled as we envisioned. By identifying those parts through manufacturing literature we could (a) use these to design functional subsystems to support the heat chamber and (b) focus our design efforts on the parts that were unique and custom (and unknown) to the solution. (See design sketch on page 44 and photo on page 153.)

Another example is the small countertop venting appliance vent we invented to capture effluent from countertop cooking equipment, clean it, and return it to the room. Once we had a basic concept and knew we could capture air around a single appliance, we had to design and test a series of capture areas and fan and motor combinations to create the right capture and air flow, and we had to test existing filter systems to clean the air adequately before addressing the appearance design aspect of the appliance. All the components except the actual capture box and hood were available commercially. In this case the process of testing resulted in a variety of interchangeable hoods for proper capture, which resulted in the awarding a second patent on this product.

## THE ROLE OF COMPONENT MANUFACTURERS

In some cases, a major component or operating system manufacturer can become essential to building your invention. A manufacturer may not initially make a component that offers exactly what you need for your solution, but they build businesses based on selling product to other manufacturers for inclusion in new products. When you can convince a component manufacturer to assist you in calculating your needs for their product, they can provide factory knowledge and assistance that's nearly impossible to hire. After you have identified a key component or system, reach out to the factories and invite them to discuss how their product can work within your new invention. Many will be willing to modify details of their components if they feel the potential for a sale is significant. If not, they are usually willing to assist for a reasonable fee. Many of these manufacturers have representatives who cover the area in which you live; they are often a good place to start. These agents often carry multiple lines of products and know other agents who carry more. They can be very valuable in sourcing the parts you need for your prototyping. Again, they make their living on selling product eventually but are often willing to assist a new inventor in the hope it will lead to future product sales. Most manufacturer websites will list their regional and local agents, representatives, or distributors.

To find manufacturers of specific types of parts, begin by searching web-based sources you find by searches. In our work we often used Thomas Register, which was an industry leader in sourcing manufacturers of just about any industrial product or component. This is now incorporated into Thomas, https://

www.thomasnet.com. It is the primary source of supplier identification for US and Canadian manufacturers. A second great source for finding components of all types and for generating ideas of what parts might be used to accomplish some function is McMaster-Carr, a distributor of over 490,000 products (https://www.mcmaster.com).

## ASSEMBLING A FULL WORKING PROTOTYPE

### Bill of Materials

When you are at a point where you are comfortable with the functioning of your subassemblies, you now want to combine the results of all that experimentation and component testing into one embodiment design and build a functional representation of your inventive solution.

You are building your invention into one connected operating prototype that satisfies all your requirements. You will be expanding your "bill of materials" in this process, which will list all buyout parts and all custom parts, including sources and costs. You will keep building and modifying your bill of materials throughout the process until you have the functional prototype you are seeking.

On buyout parts, ask the manufacturer for budget pricing at levels of quantity purchase. There should be breaks on the cost at each level of purchase quantity. On custom parts, you will have to use a rule of thumb or guidance from a manufacturer (or rep) familiar with that customization process. Custom parts may also require a onetime investment in tooling. Request quotes on these requirements when assembling your budget. The bill of materials and pricing will provide the tools to create an estimate (with assumed labor) of your manufactured costs. This will be critical to commercialization.

## Sources of Help

If you are not the type (as I am not) who can physically do this work yourself, fear not. It means you look for talent that can perform the work under your direction. There are a lot of engineers, CAD designers, and industrial designers who can assist for reasonable fees. We advertise or use university job boards to find temporary talented assistance. Sometimes we have hired some talent on "project" or "assignment" websites such as Upwork (https://www.upwork.com) or Sologig (https://www.sologig.com), and we have even sent several projects to India to an engineer who contacted us for outsource work. Local universities, colleges, and technical schools can provide talent for your efforts, and we've had some of our best results from local sources. Also check out local "maker spaces" for talent. Many communities now have these collective workshops where space is taken by multiple parties with varied disciplines to do their own work and assignments for others. These are usually talented individuals looking to start a business and build their client base. Search the web for local maker spaces, then contact the renting office for a list of participants or just visit, walk around, and talk to those people working there. For more information on this movement, contact Maker Media Inc. (http://www.makermedia.com).

One final and often overlooked source is retired individuals who want to be involved in something and don't mind earning a little extra cash. There are a lot of people out there who are retired but have active minds and talented hands to build things. Some of our best work came from retired factory workers who wanted to be a part of something new.

We eventually had our own in-house talent team, but begin as we did. Use what you can find in these sources; it's less expensive than hiring design or engineering shops (at this stage) and you personally become more involved in overseeing the prototyping, allowing you to guide your solution to actuality. Be cautious of assigning work and not monitoring it closely yourself. You are the one who knows your solution best; guide the work of others almost daily. You will be the one who will recognize errors, opportunities, and breakthroughs as the work progresses.

We've mentioned a small appliance vent project a couple times. The following photo and illustration show the early mock-up to test the concept and then the final form the invention took in a CAD 3D model. The mock-up was made from scrap metal, resized buyout parts, wood, cardboard, duct tape, and our Shop-Vac.

*Early prototype of SA Vent™ (small appliance vent).*

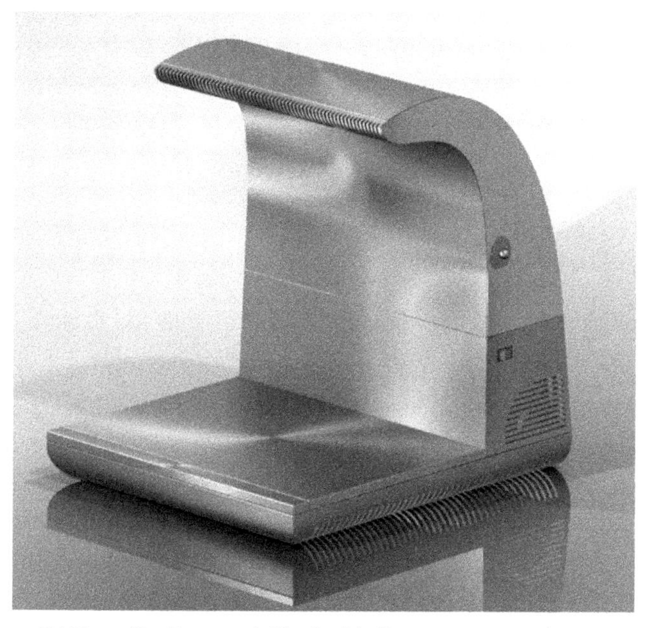

*SA Vent (by Equipex) "looks like" prototype rendering.*

## Concept Design (Your "Looks Like" Prototype)

Concept design (in my interpretation) is the process of moving into a holistic product design from prototyping and component system testing.

You know your product or service requirements, you have experimental results that have identified working components, and you now need to put them together into initial embodiment designs to evaluate and choose from. You are moving into "looks like" design to combine with your "acts like" results.

Initially this is an exercise of computer CAD modeling, which varies from full computer design in that you are not yet designing complete manufacturing specifications where every nut, bolt, screw hole, bend radius, etc., is detailed in the model. Computer modeling is dealing with the shape, look, ergonomics, and visual details of your invention. You are dealing with incorporating your subassemblies to ensure they work together and fit within your design.

At this stage, more elaborate drawings become very useful. An industrial designer, artist, or talented CAD operator using a CAD program like SolidWorks or AutoCAD Inventor and a rendering program like Adobe Illustrator can generate multiple concepts to evaluate the pros and cons for your next development stage. When you have selected one design to take forward, you enter the design development stage.

## Design Development

In this phase, you will add more detail to one selected design. You will analyze aspects of actually manufacturing or having your invention manufactured.

Things to consider are dimensions, function, form or appearance, materials, manufacturability, serviceability, ergonomics, environmental impact, and design-related reliability. In some cases consider packaging. First and foremost focus on the functionality of your invention: Does it meet your design specification? Eventually your concept design will want to have professional eyes look at it for manufacturability, aesthetics, and form. Good industrial, mechanical, and electrical designers will become very handy at the final or detailed design stage.

In this "looks like, acts like" prototyping phase, you are striving to create as close a replica of your invention's embodiment and function as possible. Your function is represented by your "acts like" prototype and your "looks like" is represented by renderings and CAD models.

## FULL "LOOKS LIKE, ACTS LIKE" (LLAL) PROTOTYPE

Depending on your invention, you may or may not want or need to develop a full ready-for-manufacturing prototype. If you are intending to manufacture your invention yourself, then it is absolutely necessary. If your invention has complexity to it, full LLAL prototyping can be very time-consuming and very costly. Over the years, we found we could initiate our patent process and commercialization process without the final embodiment of the physical invention. Often the full LLAL prototype becomes the responsibility of the ultimate manufacturer when you license your invention. If you are going into business and are using an outsource manufacturer, they can build a final LLAL for you but usually will charge you for tooling and a prototype manufacturing cost (usually 4 to 10 times more than the cost of production manufacturing).

If you need a full LLAL prototype, there are designers, model shops, and engineering shops that specialize in assisting inventors and others by building finished prototypes. Depending on your product, you may even want to engage a foreign shop to conduct prototyping if they build items similar to your invention; again, the closer you are to the process, the better. You will be able to direct and control the outcome of the work if you can be directly involved. A quick web search provides hundreds claiming to assist with prototyping and completing your invention. I am very cautious with this work; working locally has always served me well. Ideas Well Done became a prototype builder for others in addition to our invention work, but each was a valued customer that trusted us before engaging in work together. I would recommend discussing your needs with the same list of professionals in your area that I recommended earlier (local business lawyer, accounting firm, banker, venture capital firm, angel group, and others associated with local businesses). Following up on a few connections will lead you to a trusted source. Another approach is to track down potential sources for prototyping through manufacturing and engineering associations. Members of these associations are usually professional and trustworthy and can assist or guide you to viable sources for the services you need. Visit https://additivemanufacturingtoday.com/associations/?cat_id=78&view=listcats, which provides links to major associations for manufacturing and engineering.

While I won't downplay the value of a full LLAL prototype for selling and licensing activities, it may not be necessary. If your working models and renderings are adequate (and exciting enough) to convey all the value and benefit of your invention, you will be able to protect and commercialize your invention faster. If you are licensing or contracting your manufacturing to a professional manufacturing house, in all likelihood they will have to create manufacturing CAD packages particular to their equipment and processes, thus duplicating some of your effort if you were to create a full LLAL prototype. You may end up having to do this work eventually, but again, depending on your invention product, I advocate postponing the manufacturing prototype until later.

## The Water Heating Device Conclusion

The concept design phase for our water boosting device was very simple. I did a sketch linking parts and pieces and a detail of the main heater, which is a round tube with a membrane at either end. We filled the tube with a combination of carbon pellets and ceramic pellets, the pellet size being bigger than the membrane openings. On the internal walls of the tube, we put strips of titanium with a connector tab penetrating the wall of the tube and sealed against leakage and pressure. The tabs were for electrical connections. These strips of metal were to act as electrodes to pass electrical current into the water as it flowed through the tube, using the carbon pellets as electrical distributors. It took a little experimenting to get the mixture of pellets right and the electrical connections sealed against leaking, but it went quite smoothly.

The tube would have to be in a container (metal box) to conceal the electrical components. The end of the tube was fitted with water connectors to adapt to standard hot water lines typically used in plumbing installations. On the inlet side, a flow activation switch was added so that no power was provided to the booster until the hot water faucet was turned on; at that time, the electrodes were provided with power and the power was conducted by the carbon pellets and conveyed to the water volumetrically throughout the pipe, instantly heating every molecule of the water at once. The more dissolved solids in the water, the faster the water heated. The water became the heating element.

We ran into several problems in testing: first, getting the temperature just right, which resulted in numerous tests to balance power and the amount of conductive material (carbon) in the tube. Since the conductivity of water varies based on the amount of dissolved solids in the water, we needed a way to control when to stop heating based on speed of temperature increase; this was solved with a temperature sensor coupled with an algorithm to anticipate the temperature rise and act before an actual temperature cut off.

Second, the water exiting the booster tended to carry a small charge of electricity with it because of its conductivity. It would not be good to shock someone at the sink, and the appliance would not get the necessary approvals in this condition. This was unexpected and proved to be our biggest challenge. The final result was a grounded nonconductive extension to the tube, with a flow pattern allowing the water flow to change directions in contact with a grounding device, slightly reducing flow speed. To date this seems to be the best solution, but the project is ongoing. Even at this late stage, this is categorized as finding issues by experimenting and then solving them one by one, leading to a more market-worthy product.

We discovered each of these problems as we assembled and tested the prototypes. Solutions came simply by trying different things that we thought might work. The current leak solution was aided by finding one of our old patent search items that had a grounding device at a liquid exit point; we modified this concept into our design to fit our tube and membrane concept.

We realized during the process that there are a lot of other potential uses for this device, such as hot water feed to equipment (like dishwashers), thermal fluid heating for radiant space heating, and other applications, such as shower heads and localized water heating combined with central water heating, where each location can take a lower temperature feed from water heating and create the exact temperature needed at that location (120°F for hand sinks, 180°F for sanitary rinsing, for example).

In May 2016, we were awarded US Patent 9,345,069 for "Heat generation and exchange device incorporating a mixture of conductive and dielectric particles." We sold the rights to this development and several others to a manufacturer maintaining a royalty arrangement in addition to the selling price.

## A SHORT HISTORY OF PATENTS IN AMERICA

As an inventor you will be constantly involved with the process of patent prosecution, both in the United States and in foreign countries. To get you started, this essay is a short history of patents in America.

The profession of inventor in America could be argued to have begun with the first patents issued on American soil in the Colonial period. There were no specific laws governing the protection of a new invention. Inventors could take their case to the Colonial governments and request the exclusive rights to commercialization for something they created. The first record of a right granted in North America may have taken place in 1641 by the Massachusetts General Court to Samuel Winslow, providing exclusivity to a process for making salt. Some accounts claim this as the first American patent, before patents as an official creation existed.

Other accounts claim the first "patent" issued in America was to an English immigrant named Joseph Jenks on March 6, 1646, in Boston, for the *manifactures of engins of mils to go by water for speedy dispatch of much worke with few hands.* Jenks was a skilled ironworker who immigrated to America in 1642 to help establish the first American ironworks in Saugus, Massachusetts. He also cut the dies for the first coins minted in Boston (1652) and built the first American fire engine (1654). However, still other accounts claim Joseph Jenckes (slightly different spelling) was awarded the first patent by the General Court of Massachusetts, for making a scythe, but give this guy the credit for the first fire engines as well. They are the same person, but the record-keeping of patent allowances had yet to be standardized.

The first "official" patent issued in 1790 by the US government was to an American-born inventor, Vermont native Samuel Hopkins. He was granted US Patent 1 under the new US patent statute signed into law by President Washington a few months before Hopkins's patent was issued. The patent was for an improvement "in the making of Pot ash and Pearl ash by a new Apparatus and Process." The process produced an ingredient used in fertilizer. The patent was signed by President George Washington, Attorney General Edmund Randolph, and Secretary of State Thomas Jefferson. Hopkins also received the first Canadian patent from the Parliament of Lower Canada in 1791, issued to "Angus MacDonnel, a Scottish soldier garrisoned at Quebec City and to Samuel Hopkins, a Vermonter" for processes to make potash and soap from wood ash.

The first official legislation protecting intellectual property was part of the Constitution of the United States adopted on September 17, 1787. The Patent Act of 1790 was the first official statute for the issue of patents and was titled "An Act to Promote the Progress of Useful Arts." This act prevented foreigners from obtaining patents in the United States. The act called for an examination process by the Secretary of State, the Secretary of War, and the Attorney General; it took two of the three to get an approved patent. It was finally determined that this process took too long–up to several months–and these people had more important things to do. Ironically the patent process can

*continued*

now take three years or more due to the number of patents processed and a sometimes inefficient process for approval.

Several other patent acts attempted to improve the patent process, not always succeeding, until the Patent Act of 1836 reformed the previous acts and eliminated problems created by earlier attempts at reform. This act created the Patent Office of the United States under the State Department. This office issued new patent numbers with all previous patents being renumbered with the suffix "X."

Currently patents are being issued with patent numbers in the nine millions. In 2015, over 589,000 utility patent applications were received by the USPTO (United States Patent and Trademark Office) and 298,407 utility patents (inventions) were issued. The numbers do not directly correlate, since few patents issue in less than one year. In the years 1996 to 2005, it is estimated that 55.8 percent of the applications filed issued as patents (discounting continuation patents that emerge as additional patents on an issued patent).

Some argue that the lone inventor is gone and that now all invention takes place in a lab or a university or engineering department. The Census Bureau eliminated "inventor" as an occupation in 1940. But this could not be further from the truth.

Take a trip on the internet and visit sites related to independent inventing, which continues to thrive in the United States and elsewhere. Look at the founders of new technology-based businesses and social businesses; most have an invention beginning, as industries did in the 18th and 19th centuries. Some inventions may be apps, video games, or aspects of artificial intelligence or services, like home sharing or ride hailing instead of tools, instruments, or steamboats, but that's how invention advances us. It's educational to follow *Fortune* magazine's annual article on 40 under 40 Hottest Young Stars in Business and similar lists in *Businessweek, Forbes,* and the stories in *MIT Technology Review.* Note how many are based on an invention of an idea, a business concept, or a product. Invention is everywhere and growing in importance.

• PART •

# INVENTION PROTECTION

• CHAPTER 12 •

# Invention and Patent Process

**STEP 16:** Protect your work; patent your inventive solution.

**WHEN INVENTING, A** patent application and the eventual issue of a patent are the best protection for your efforts and the most valuable assets for earning money or raising money for a business effort.

I have cautioned throughout the text to get noncompete, nonuse, nondisclosure agreements (NDAs) from everyone you reveal any inventive piece of your effort to. If you reveal your patent work to the public in any way prior to filing some form of patent application, your rights to file for a patent will expire in 365 days from your public exposure. Even showing your idea to a friend, a parent, or a potential service provider you intend to hire can start the clock running if you don't execute an NDA. By exposure you can also alert competitors and risk the filing of a competitive patent, nullifying yours. The way to prevent this from happening is by getting an NDA signed by everyone you discuss your solution with. This now classifies as a nonpublic disclosure and you are protected by the terms of the agreement. There are different forms for different purposes: one for general disclosure of information; one for hiring outside firms or individuals to do work for you; and one for your employees, who should sign a patent agreement where they agree to confidentiality outside the firm and agree that all invention work will be assigned to the benefit of your business or you. Provide the individual with a copy of the agreement signed by both of you and follow up with a copy emailed to your lawyer.

Since the earliest days, almost all invention was based on the hope of realizing a financial benefit or protection from another party realizing a financial benefit from an inventor's original creation. This chapter is intended to help you prepare to financially benefit and to protect the work and the creativity you have invested in your invention.

When people talk about invention, they usually are thinking about the issuing of a patent. A patent is not an invention. A patent is a grant to own a monopoly for a period of time on what you have invented. This monopoly is intended to give you a commercial advantage for up to 20 years. It is also a vehicle to communicate all the inventive insights you have created to others so they can improve on your invention, advancing technology. This is an objective of the patent system.

An invention doesn't need to be patented, although it is most often advisable, especially if someone can acquire your invented item and reverse engineer it. It is also hard to convince anyone to license your invention or otherwise fund it if it is not patented.

An invention, according to the US Patent and Trademark Office (USPTO), is issued for the creation of a new and useful process, machine, manufacture, or composition of matter, or a new and useful improvement thereof. This description references utility patents.

The USPTO classifies inventions into types: utility, design, and plant. What we deal with in this book are the inventions covered by utility patents. Approximately 90 percent of the patent documents issued by the USPTO in recent years have been utility patents, which are also referred to as "patents of invention."

A patent application incorporates the invention and the problem addressed; it details the invention in drawings, description, and use definition. A patent also describes how to use, build, or manufacture your invention in detail. In many patents, a list of earlier patents or other literature dealing with similar solutions will be listed; this is the "prior art" we have referenced earlier. The prior art will include a listing submitted by you as discovered in the invention development process, plus it will include prior art references found by the patent examiner in his process. You will have to defend your invention to the patent examiner as not being obvious in the disclosures of this prior art. You will do this by responding to "office actions" as submitted by the examiner. You will only reply to those he chooses to use to argue "obviousness" based on one or a combination of prior art citations.

A patent is intended to provide you with time to take your invention into commercialization or to assign it to someone else to commercialize. Hopes are that you create sufficient business to make it unreasonable for a competitor to try to duplicate your success once your coverage expires. Also, be advised that a patent is particular to the country of issue; it does not protect you from someone duplicating your invention in another country, but it protects you from that duplicate product being sold in this country or any country where you have patent protection.

There are different filing possibilities that you can use depending on what will serve your commercial needs the most. More often than not we would file a "provisional patent" application. This can be done much earlier in the development process and allows the commercialization effort to begin at once. It is much simpler to file and less costly. The full submission work doesn't have to be complete in every detail. We have filed with sketches instead of formal patent drawings, even photographs of prototypes in some cases. Once filed (the day of) you are officially "patent pending" and your invention will be protected from that day forward if your patent eventually issues. You can label any commercial product covered by this filing as "patent pending," thus notifying anyone looking to duplicate your work that they can be subject to litigation. The drawbacks are that you have only 365 days from that filing of a provisional patent application to file the formal nonprovisional patent application or you lose the right to claim a patent on your invention. No extensions are granted. Also you cannot add any new discoveries or inventive details to your nonprovisional filing, so you must be quite sure you have all your data and discoveries revealed in the provisional application. The provisional application never gets examined for patentability; it simply gives you an earlier date of claiming invention, limited protection, and a jump-start on commercialization if you choose. It does establish your date and prevents other similar filings from being able to receive coverage, since your filing becomes prior art for anyone who follows.

Your nonprovisional filing is the formal patent application for examination. It must include a specification, which includes a description of your invention and preferably background information. It will include formal drawings, charts, and graphs as necessary to convey all the information about your invention, and these must conform to very specific format requirements required by the USPTO. It must include an oath or declaration of invention and the proper fees for examination and patent search by the USPTO. Most importantly it must include claims in a very specific format and order. Generally there are primary claims, which should be very broad, and dependent claims, which should be more limiting and detail expanded attributes of the primary claims. The broader the primary claim allowed, the more protection afforded. It becomes harder for others to invent around your invention. If rejected (likely, since almost every filing is rejected at least once, usually more), a broad claim can narrow its broadness by pulling in and incorporating one or more of the dependent claims, making it a part of a primary claim. I do not recommend that anyone not formally trained prepare and submit a nonprovisional application. There are too many subtleties that can rob you of protection, unnecessarily limit your protection, or even cause the patent not to issue. The best approach is to hire a patent agent or lawyer to assist you. A patent agent is less costly and sometimes just as effective in preparing your filing and helping you address the actions of the examiner, but only a patent lawyer can defend you in court if necessary. Both have the same license to represent you within the USPTO. I use both depending on the complexity of the invention. A good place to begin your search for representation is the National Association of Patent Practitioners (NAPP) at https://www.napp.org.

Often a nonprovisional patent application can sit for months or even years without examination beginning. You are officially patent pending in this time period; however, you would not be able to prosecute for infringement until your patent issues. You can put others on notice that you have protection if you see actions you believe violate your claims and thus warn the offending party that they could be in a position of infringement. If they knowingly make and sell an infringing product after being notified, then you are likely to be awarded increased damages winning a lawsuit after issue of your patent.

If your invention has commercial potential internationally, you can file your nonprovisional application as a PCT (Paris Cooperation Treaty) patent application. You can file it at the USPTO, just like you would file your nonprovisional patent application for only the United States. You can even file in another country initially and later request examination in the USPTO. By filing your original nonprovisional patent application as a PCT, you will be filing and receiving protection in 151 countries initially. (This is the number of countries participating as of September 8, 2016.) This provides limited protection for up to 30 months and is useful and helpful if international coverage is desirable. If you take this route, you eventually have to request inspection in each of the countries where you wish a patent to issue. We would typically request examination in the United States as part of the application. It is not likely you will want all 151 countries (and foreign filings can get very expensive), but if it's likely your patent has commercial value in certain countries or that there will be considerable demand for your invention in foreign countries, then a PCT filing can give you limited protection while you explore the market and begin commercialization. The PCT patent protection is also advisable if you intend to license to a company doing business in other countries. If you are in license talks with a company wishing coverage in other countries, you can often negotiate the costs of individual country examination into a license deal. If you simply file a US patent first without requesting PCT options, you have one year to file for foreign coverage, after which you are prohibited from doing so.

When you file your nonprovisional patent application, your application will be categorized into an "art unit" at the USPTO, where similar applications are examined and eventually your application will be assigned to an examiner. The examiner assigned to your application will judge utility or usefulness of your invention; he or she will determine that it is new or novel and that it is nonobvious to a person of ordinary skill in the art at the time of the invention.

It is important to discuss art units with your patent professional before writing claims. They should know what is out of favor and how to work around it. For example, the success rate of applications decreased following 2005 because of restrictions placed on drugs and certain medical instruments, computers, and communications filings. It is important when filing that your agent or attorney writes your claims in a way to avoid currently out-of-favor art units within the US patent office. I once lost two years without any significant action on a deserving patent until we applied pressure to change art units (an unusual occurrence) after which our patent issued within weeks.

The invention process is not necessarily logical or predictable; the examiner assigned to your application has a lot of control and will typically reject your first attempt with reference to one or multiple prior art patents declaring your invention "obvious." The best advice I can give here is to have the help of an experienced patent agent or lawyer to assist in the process of countering the examiner's rejections until you receive an allowance. Persistence is an important attribute when seeking a patent, and with convincing arguments countering the rejections of your work, you will prevail—provided you have legitimate inventive properties.

Many applications will go back and forth with this process, with the examiner combining prior art, sometimes in very creative ways, to reject your invention until you receive a "final rejection." Final isn't final; it's the point where you are required to request "continued examination." When a final rejection is received, you will counter the current arguments and pay a fee and file a continued examination form. This basically allows the examiner more time (paid for by the continued examination fee) to further examine your application. After final rejection or often at the point of continued examination, I have requested, along with my patent agent or attorney, a phone conversation with the examiner. The question "What are you willing to accept?" or something similar at this point often results in constructive guidance of changes to your wording in the claims where the examiner will be willing to accept your invention and provide an allowance. I recently went through this entire process into continued examination on an application. In talking with the agent, we changed one word in our claims where we inserted the word "completely" before every use of the word "divided," and we were awarded almost all of our claims as otherwise written. You cannot add any new material to an application once filed, but we clearly showed in our drawings that our invention had two compartments "completely" divided one from the other. All the examiner's discoveries of prior art had two compartments, but none were "completely" divided.

All this examination and maneuvering takes time; you are also using up some of your 20 years of exclusivity during this period. A couple of procedures can assist in speeding the prosecution process. The first is for people over 65 or in poor health who can request that their application be "made special." When granted, the application time can be reduced considerably. The patent office does not charge for this service. The second is what is called the "Track One" filing. You can pay a fee to get your application prioritized. In theory, this will allow you to get a final disposition within 12 months. It can go longer if you request continued examination in the event of a rejection. The cost for Track One filing is currently set at an additional $4,800 (50 percent discount for small entities) on top of normal filing fees. This is basically a method for the USPTO to earn additional fees for granting a privilege. Some filers are content to have their applications drag on and to use the benefits of patent pending as their marketing strength.

It is good to study the patent process and to be as knowledgeable as possible, but my advice as mentioned above is not to try the process on your own without professional assistance. I tried that once and failed completely, losing what might have been a valuable patent. Be advised, if you buy a book on filing patents, get the most recent edition and check to make sure it is written around the new America Invents Act passed September 16, 2011, with varying effective dates following this date. This act transformed the US patent process from a "first to invent" patent system into a "first to file" system. One thing this means is that if more than one person is working on a similar solution to a problem, the first to file common claims owns it. It's a lot more complex than that, but be advised to protect your work as you go; learn and follow the rules of the patent process and you will be protected.

There are a couple of other patent application terms you should be familiar with. One is called a "divisional patent." This occurs when an examiner rejects your application because he or she determines that it has more than one invention revealed (it doesn't mean the examiner will allow any of them). You will then be required to choose which "invention" to have the examiner evaluate and prosecute for a patent determination. You have the right to file an additional application using most of your same filing material, but with different claims on the divisional you remove from the original filing claims. In this way, you may end up with multiple patents on your invention, making it more valuable. A second term is a "continuation patent." Up until the point where your patent application is issued or abandoned, you can file additional claims not claimed in your original application. These applications have a new date of invention filing (the filing date) and are examined separately from the original filing. You can file continuation patents up to the day before issue of your original filing. This does not mean you can file on new discoveries not revealed in the original specification or drawings; you cannot add new material once filed. It does mean that inventive material in your original filing that was not placed in a claim can now be used in a continuation patent.

## THE KERNEL OF INVENTION

### • Sir William Perkin (1838-1907) •

**In this profile, we find that almost anything can be an invention and that one breakthrough invention can become the motivation for multiple other developments by other inventors. We also again experience the mistake as a method to discovery.**

**In his hugely entertaining book *Mauve*, Simon Garfield recounts the life of William Perkin, who is credited with inventing a color that changed the world.**

**William Perkin visited Leeds, England, in his twenties to seek out the residence of his late grandfather Thomas Perkin. Thomas had become a leather worker in Leeds after leaving his family farm. Exploring the house, William found a cellar filled with what appeared to be a working laboratory. William discov-**

ered that in addition to working leather his grandfather had a pastime as an alchemist, attempting to turn base metal into gold. William examined the still, forge, and bottles of dirty burnt mixtures of various concoctions with interest and surprise, since his personal direction had also taken him away from family pursuits toward chemistry.

In his youth, William had no idea what he wanted to do with his life. He was a good student and indulged in many hobbies. He took an interest in photography for a while and thought he might want to pursue something of an artistic vocation. He later became interested in engineering and mechanics and related scientific developments that all seemed to be moving rapidly. He had entertained music in his teens and thought of traveling as a quartet with his brother and two sisters.

At 13, William began attending the strict City of London School with 600 other boys. It was one of the few schools that had a course in chemistry. Chemistry at the time was thought to be of little value, but it captured William's imagination. William applied himself in his newfound passion. The teacher, Thomas Hall, noticed William's interest and enlisted him to help prepare experiments for his lectures. Hall further suggested that he might undertake some of the safer experiments at home. William was soon attending scientific lectures throughout London; through a recommendation, he was personally invited to attend a lecture by Michael Faraday, the English scientist famous for his experimentations of electromagnetism and electrochemistry, which helped solidify William's desire to pursue scientific discovery. Over the objections of William's father, Hall recommended that William at age 15 enroll to study chemistry with August Wilhelm von Hofmann, the renowned first director at the Royal College of Chemistry in London. William's father was eventually convinced, and in 1853, William began his chemistry education in earnest.

This was the age of gas in London, gas made from the distillation of coal. Heating the combustible material in closed

*continued*

vessels without oxygen resulted in not only coal gas but also several dangerous by-products, most notably sulfur compounds and a sizeable amount of coal tar, originally considered waste. These wastes were randomly discarded, polluting water sources, killing fish, and fouling the land. Eventually new uses were found; for example, the water residue from the gas process was used in creating sulfuric acid. Charles Macintosh in the 1820s devised a way to use the coal tar to waterproof cloth, first creating a raincoat, later known as the Macintosh. Various combinations became wood and metal coatings, a sewage treatment disinfectant, and subjects of experimentation with road surfacing.

The time was early in the development of chemistry as a science; chemists were just learning the components that made up many of the compounds and how they formed. But element science was not well understood. Breakthroughs resulted in the solvent naphtha being isolated in coal tar. Benzene was found to be a component of naphtha and later such materials as toluidine and aniline were identified as coal tar by-products.

Aniline was of the greatest interest to Hofmann, who spent a good deal of time investigating its possibilities, sharing his enthusiasm with his students. Hofmann's primary pursuit was to create quinine in a laboratory setting. Quinine was the only treatment for malaria, which was rampant in the world, including England and the English colonies. Natural quinine was limited in availability and came from one plant–the cinchona tree found only in Peru and Bolivia. Hofmann felt that through the manipulation of chemical compounds he could create a lab version of quinine. It was at the time the most sought-after drug in the world. He recognized that quinine resembled naphthalidine, which could be made in quantity from the conversion of naphtha, all initially coming from coal gas. Quinine contained two molecules absent in naphthalidine, hydrogen and oxygen, both found in water. His hypothesis was that, through some experimentation, water and naphthalidine could create artificial quinine. However, the solution was elusive. When William Perkin recognized the importance of the idea, he began to work on the solution as well.

Perkin was still a novice chemist and experimented in his home laboratory with the simple processes of adding or subtracting materials to find a compound that appeared similar to what he was trying to create. In one such experiment, he attempted to alter an artificial base into natural alkaloid quinine, but instead of the clear liquid of quinine, he ended up with a reddish powder. The result failed, so he chose to experiment with a simpler base, aniline. In this case, he ended up with a black substance. Instead of abandoning the failed compound, he conducted experiments on it to assess what he had created. His unexpected find was that when the black substance was treated with spirits, purified, and dried, he could separate out a color-replicating dye; the new color was eventually called "mauve." Perkin, by accident followed by curiosity, experimentation, and observation, invented a color that would change the world.

Colors and color sources had been discovered for millennia, but most were from natural sources, were expensive and time-consuming to produce, and were often limited in source locations and supply. Furthermore many required complex, labor-intensive processes to create a finished dyed product. It was recognized in the dyeing trade that a dye you made in a lab, on demand, with purity and consistency of strength, held a valuable potential—provided it produced consistent and lasting results and was a desirable color.

Perkin communicated with some dyers and felt encouraged that his creation could be a viable product. However, he feared that by entering enterprise as a manufacturer, he would forever be banned from the true scientific research community that he loved. If he failed, he could not return to the laboratory due to the stigma of a researcher pursuing commercial exploitation of his discovery. He was 18 at this time. He had no experience, guidance, or expertise to enter business and succeed; his product

*continued*

and procedures were not perfected, he had no idea how to reach or convince the market, and multiple other obstacles stood in his way. But he jumped in anyway. He took action to do what he needed to do as an entrepreneur to ensure the success of his invention.

The business story that follows his invention details the struggles of a start-up with an unknown product and provides good lessons for those of you entering business for the first time. One lesson he learned is that his failure to get a French patent for his discovery (because he did not file in the required time following the British patent) allowed a competitor to use his process to produce his product and sell it against him. Mauve became a success and so did Perkin's business for a period of time as he expanded processes and colors. The world of fashion exploded with color. Perkin's impact on the dye trades, fashion, other color uses like wallpaper and even the entire British economy are unquestioned. What he did to develop a product spurred greater interest in the use of coal tar and coal by-products to develop commercial products, and through his success the acceptance of organic chemistry as an exciting and practical (even profitable) profession was established, and this is the greatest contribution of Perkin's success in leading a movement in dye development. His contribution to the British national gross domestic product was substantial. He was successful and a wealthy man at 38, when he stepped back from both commercial and academic notoriety to continue his research in private in his newly built dream home. His contributions were to continue, but for our purposes, we have seen the lessons that a pursuit of curiosity and a systematic process of experimentation and examination can lead to substantial inventive success.

The work of William Perkin led directly or indirectly to many important discoveries in unrelated fields such as medicine and perfume development, photography, and explosives, to name a few. Also many other artificial colors were developed using related processes as developed by Perkin.

We learn from Perkin:

- Find and pursue what you are passionate about.
- Emerging fields are ripe for invention.
- Start by gathering basic knowledge.
- Hypothesis proves things wrong as well as right and therefore serves as a starting point for further investigation and experimentation.
- Be curious about surprising results.
- Experimentation and observation are keys to invention.
- To benefit from invention, you must take action to innovate once discovery is achieved.
- Protect your markets.

SOURCES: Simon Garfield's book *Mauve* and internet references.

• PART •

# COMMERCIALIZATION

• CHAPTER 13 •

# Prepare for Commercialization

**STEP 17:** Prepare your product for the market.

## ACQUIRE TESTING AND APPROVALS NEEDED

Either you or a licensed manufacturing partner will want to do two things before a full product launch into the marketplace:

1. Test your product with real market conditions or actual consumers.
2. Submit your product to the agencies required by your particular industry to receive the approvals necessary for acceptance in the market.

The first is a wise step; the second, a requirement.

If you are headed into manufacturing or contract manufacturing (see next chapter), and provided you have built full working models of your invention and have a rendered design model, you will want to take these steps now. If your commercialization effort is to partner or license your product with a third party, it is likely these steps can become part of what the third party is required to do in a licensing contract.

## FIELD TRIALS OR MARKET TESTING

Depending on the nature of your product, your finished prototype may allow you to make arrangements for real-world evaluation of your solution through field trials or market testing. A field trial is more relevant to a machine or systems-type product. In these cases, you need to find a willing and cooperative business or institution with interest in the type of solution you have, and they need to agree to a period of testing. Your requirements for them would include allowing observation of your system or product in trial and writing evaluations as to the performance of your system or product during or following the testing.

The best way to arrange a field trial is to approach appropriate locations directly. You have probably identified likely candidates during your assessment work, but if not, establish some criteria that you feel will give you the field trial answers you need, such as what works, what doesn't, and what you would improve. Is this a product you would buy? There are dozens of questions you can come up with related to the future success of your invention. Another approach is to contact dealers or distributors that handle products that fit into your invention's category of product. They can provide a level of assessment but also help set up field trials with their existing customer base. Their customers trust and know them, so this can get you into sites that you might not get into on your own.

We developed a new sanitation product for hospital monitoring. We knew the need was there from our detailed research early in the process, but we did not know how the system would be viewed or accepted in actual hospital situations. We approached the head nurse in charge of infectious disease prevention at a local hospital and invited her to view a demonstration. She became our champion at the hospital. She convinced administration, nurses, and engineering that, if successful, this system would solve big problems with acquired infections. We were accepted and allowed to conduct a full-scale field trial. This allowed us to improve aspects of our product to adjust to real-world conditions before market entry.

You need a formal agreement to protect yourself, your product, and the tester. The agreement should state that the product is new and does not include formal approvals (if it doesn't) and include a "hold harmless" clause for both parties. The agreement also has to incorporate a section for nondisclosure and nonuse if your patent has not yet been issued. It's advisable to get legal assistance in writing this agreement. In some cases, a testing partner might be willing to participate at several levels of your development, providing valuable input to the design and performance of your final product. In the hospital field trial, we also had to seek clearance from patients, since they were involved in the system testing.

Market testing is more for consumer products and less complex inventions, where you may have a group of testers assessing your prototype. You still need an agreement from each tester. The agreement will be a little less complex, but it still needs clauses for hold harmless, nondisclosure, and nonuse. Again, this is an area where it is important to engage legal help. You might conduct this testing in consumer homes, on-site at a retailer, or in monitored focus groups. A formal evaluation by each tester will be very useful.

In some cases, you may be able to actually sell product or conduct in-store demonstrations as part of your field testing, as in the case of a consumable product or a wearable product. If so, it is advisable to get all necessary product approvals prior to conducting these tests. Again a direct approach is good if you identify appropriate locations for your testing. If you engage a marketing firm or an ad firm as part of your team for market entry, they often can arrange testing sites and focus groups for customer testing. Your success at field testing and market testing is adding value to your invention. The more success you have, the more valuable your invention becomes.

## PRODUCT APPROVALS

Product approvals vary according to your product category and include such agencies as Underwriters Laboratories (UL) or equivalent and the

National Sanitation Foundation (NSF). Depending on your product, you may need approvals from the Food and Drug Administration (FDA). You should identify the agencies that are pertinent to your invention category during your research phase. Many of the manuals and training materials they provide can become aids to your creation and design process.

There are literally many hundreds of testing authorities and product certification bodies and each product type has its own collection of required or desirable tests. In addition, most testing bodies are particular to countries, so if your product is to be international, most countries will require some form of testing and approval for doing business in that country. Some states, with some products, require state-level testing.

There are product certification accreditation bodies and standards agencies, and they can be useful in tracking approvals for your industry. The American National Standards Institute (ANSI) at https://www.ansi.org and United Accreditation Foundation (UAF) at https://uafaccreditation.org are two examples. Most product certification bodies are accredited to the International Organization for Standardization (ISO), which can also be of assistance for tracking down your needed approvals at https://www.iso.org/home.html.

You can learn a lot at these organizations, but I suspect in your assessment work you encountered references to approvals appropriate to your industry. I was always able to track down necessary approvals with a few phone calls within the industry or by examining related products. My approach to identifying necessary approval agencies in an industry was to inspect a related product and check its rating plate, usually on the back or underside of a product but sometimes on a door frame or inside cavity. The plates list the approvals carried by the product. Look at several because some are mandatory and some are selective. When a product wasn't available, I would research competitor or industry specification sheets, which usually list the agencies these products are approved for.

• • •

## LIFE CYCLE AND CRADLE-TO-GRAVE TESTING

Each type of product will require different degrees of testing in order to be accepted in the marketplace. While this is not mandatory testing that is required for approvals, it is the type of testing that will assist in market acceptance. Life cycle testing is most important for a machine or appliance, since it can identify maintenance or reliability issues before you are in the market, saving the aggravation and costs associated with recalls and replacement. Labs have methods and machinery that can accelerate testing so years of wear and tear on your product can be assessed in days or weeks.

You can also find labs to test software, materials, and chemicals to identify possible market hurdles.

You will find sources for testing by a simple web search for "testing labs." Have a detailed description of your product and market ready to provide. If you locate local labs, we found it advisable to visit them to interview and to learn more about their methods. It is often tempting to avoid this cost, but it is advisable to hire a lab to do this testing to prove reliability over time, and to find weak areas to improve before formal marketing. You not only save a lot of headaches, but the reports you receive will help you sell your product or license your patent. If testing labs are not easily identified in your area, reach out to a noncompetitive manufacturer in the industry you are working in or to the managing director of an industry association; a few phone calls will put you on the right track.

Another popular testing procedure that is important to market success for machinery or appliances is termed "cradle-to-grave" testing and is a form of life cycle testing. In these tests, the lab assesses the environmental impact of your product in all stages of its life from raw materials to manufacturing, to customer use and finally to disposal. This is an important marketing tool for some products.

• CHAPTER 14 •

# Commercialization

**STEP 18:** Determine how you will commercialize your invention.

**NOW THE REAL** fun begins. Not that inventing isn't fun; it is a lot of fun. But seeing money come in your door daily, weekly, or monthly is the reward for executing the fun of inventing—and it too is fun.

What do you want to do with your invention? You have options: some of your options may be personal and some may be driven by the industry or business your invention serves. In this chapter, we will discuss how innovation and invention connect and how value is created with invention. We will outline your basic choices for commercialization and guide you on some of the steps to take in your chosen direction.

In my mind, I link invention with innovation, in that when applied to meaningful results an invention delivers innovation and thus value to its users. This is also when an invention becomes truly valuable to its inventor. The economy of the United States is built on innovation after innovation replacing prior innovations. Invention commercialized creates innovation. Harold Evans said it best in his book *They*

*Made America: From the Steam Engine to the Search Engine: Two Centuries of Innovators* when he wrote, "It is not simply invention; it is inventiveness put to use."

At this stage, with your invention well developed and protected, you need to confront the question of method to market and complete the task of connecting your invention with true innovation. I will explain.

An innovator seeks to apply understanding and inventive solutions to problems to create usefulness and financial value often through enterprise. In *The Lever of Riches*, economic historian Joel Mokyr, a member of the Lemelson-MIT Program, an organization that promotes the power of invention to improve lives, has stated that "without invention, innovation will eventually exhaust itself."[4] I agree with this wholeheartedly, but I will also add that without innovation, invention is worthless. The lifeblood of invention is financial success for whoever advances the invention into a financial innovation.

Innovating is about changing what exists into new and more valuable products, processes, systems, and technology and thus increasing earnings and value or reducing costs and building value. Invention is about creating something that doesn't exist. It seems mysterious to many because invention is dealing with the unknown, or more precisely creating the unknown. The use of an invention may not be obvious to those who view it. But when they are shown how it creates value, it becomes interesting. Innovation is applying something in a new way to create a better, more valuable result. Too many worthy inventions have died because the inventor did nothing with them to create the means to deliver value. You should be proud of your efforts. It's a great accomplishment to invent. But you now owe it to yourself and those who will benefit from your invention to build financial value from your creation—your work isn't done until you do.

To become a successful inventor, you must make your inventions pay for your thoughts, your time, and your investment by finding a way to make them useful to others and commercially valuable.

Thomas Edison was constantly aware of the necessary connection between invention and innovation. While not exclusively motivated by

4 The Lemelson-MIT Program is funded by the Lemelson Foundation, which exists to "improve lives through invention" (http://www.lemelson.org/).

money, he recognized that his continued work and inventing depended on having successful inventions that produced revenue. Therefore, he selected his problems based on their monetary possibilities. Unless you are independently wealthy this is a good approach.

## BUILDING VALUE

The value of your invention lies in its ability to create business and revenue for yourself or others (preferably both). To some extent its value is also enhanced based on whether others are able to compete with your invention.

I view the successful invention platform as having three legs holding it up: one is the invention and its patent; one is the embodiment of the patent in tangible form (the "looks like, acts like" prototype); and the third is marketplace entry (and success). Each leg adds more worth to your invention.

Success in securing a patent adds considerable value to your efforts. With patent examination sometimes taking three years or more, it usually isn't prudent to wait for a patent to issue to begin commercialization. However, you are protected from competition using your invention by having a patent-pending status.

To a third party (licensor) interested in licensing your invention, a pending patent doesn't provide the assurance (and value) that an issued patent does. However, a deal can usually be created pending issue of one or more patents or other pending applications. This occasionally results in a product going to market before a patent issue but with less compensation should the patent fail to issue. This is where it is advisable to continue to file continuation patents until one or more of the patents issues; it extends the patent-pending coverage until all applications are processed or one issues and can extend the time royalties are paid.

Having workable models of your invention adds a level of value and allows potential licensors, acquirers, or partners to see your solution and better understand its implications. Many people don't fully comprehend value from words or pictures, but when they see something in physical form, they can understand its value to them much better.

If you can get your product to market successfully on your own, even at a small level as in a field trial or localized sales, then you are at a point to negotiate a much more valuable contract to sell, license, or partner. Satisfied users lend credibility to your market assumptions and value calculations. If your product is in the market, your invention's value will then be based on an estimate of the total market value of your invention over the life of the patents, a much more meaningful place from which to negotiate.

## TYPES OF INVENTION COMMERCIALIZATION

Until you establish a path for your invention to be commercialized in some fashion you have nothing more than your solution embodied in a nice patent document. To be valuable to the world and to you, it must convince others of its value. Value must be created by you or by others with whom you cooperate. Like Stephen Key, mentioned on pages 7 and 8, your first invention could pay for all your invention work to follow, as did Key's rotating label product. It could allow you to build a team of support people to assist in your developments as it did with my invention business, Ideas Well Done, or it could be the tool you use to raise capital to start your business commercializing your invention yourself; all the options are open to you.

One good invention can lead to a family of related inventions and to continued innovation and invention in the same field as your first invention. Or you may choose to solve problems in multiple disciplines as you continue to invent. The fact is, in order to continue to invent, you must continue to invest time, energy, and money. You can choose different paths to commercialization depending on your makeup, desires, and ambition.

### Build a Business: Manufacturing Your Product

You can choose to take your invention and build a business around it. I detailed earlier how one of my commercialization efforts did just this.

With one invention, eventually adding a couple more, we built a national brand in commercial food-service equipment steamers, eventually 15 related models. Building a successful business can build wealth and can be very rewarding in many ways. It can be the most lucrative return on your inventing investment. It can also fail. It can also be overwhelming in its details and demands on you. Building a manufacturing business requires a big investment, usually on an ongoing basis as growth takes capital. None of this is meant as a deterrent; it is often why people invent in the first place. In my experience, there were a lot of stressful days and frustrations along the way. We made it to success, but in a small yet satisfying and rewarding way. The one big frustration I had was that the daily demands of running a manufacturing, sales, and service business left little time for the creative efforts, which were my calling. Selling the product line and patents after eight years was good for us because it allowed us to cash out our value and provide capital to create a business model that perfectly fit what we wanted to do (and to also collect royalties on the products that we sold). Having had the business start-up and success also helped further cement our position in an industry that then became the focus of our inventions. This was very valuable.

## Build a Business: Contracting Your Manufacturing and Focusing on Marketing, Sales, and Customer Service

An alternate method of building a business around your invention and its products is to contract your manufacturing to a contract manufacturer who will build your product exclusively for you. You can then focus on building a sales and support organization. You can contract full-product production or have all parts made by a few manufacturers and set up a simple assembly operation. Depending on the type of product you create, there are firms that will build products for you. Again depending on your product you might contract locally or have your product built in another country. Locally your component or material vendors and representatives generally know of the firms you might contact. We had some success with soliciting help from the US embassies in countries where we thought a possible manufacturing partner might exist. Trade shows in other countries are also an excellent way to make contacts and source both component parts and contract manufacturing. An outsource manufacturing method still allows you to build the worth that comes with building a business that can provide substantial income and wealth when you choose to sell the organization, provided you are adequately successful. It's important to recognize that by outsourcing manufacturing you are typically reducing your profit margin unless your product is unique enough to command a premium price. This is because the contract manufacturer needs to make a profit, which reduces your margin. On the other hand, you reduce the investment in start-up manufacturing and the risk of manufacturing complications in the beginning of your business effort.

With this method you can also transition into full manufacturing (adding worth to your business) when sales and profits hit a level to support the transition.

There is considerable risk in both methods of building a business around your invention. It is also where your greatest return potential exists. In our steamer business, we executed a hybrid: we had major parts manufactured by specialty manufacturing companies, some outside the United States, and we set up an assembly shop of our own. We manufactured some parts but no complicated manufacturing, just assemble, test, ship, and take care of the customer. There is not one way that is best; it really is about what you are aiming for and what you feel is best for you.

## LICENSING

Another method to commercializing your invention is to license your patent, or a product based on your patent, to one or more manufacturers. If your patent is such that it can be applied to multiple (usually noncompeting) products, you can license to any number of manufacturers. This can be a very lucrative method for inventors to commercialize their creations. It is not easy to break into licensing, but it is done often enough to allow a new player to find a way to open the right door.

If you are inventing in a field where you are known, your effort can be a lot easier. One thing to keep in mind: licensing is not selling your patent rights; it is allowing another party to further develop a product and pay you a royalty on every unit sold for the life of the patent and often the life of any improvement patent (regardless of who invented the improvement, you or the licensor). Often you can negotiate an up-front fee in addition to the royalty to repay you for efforts and costs incurred to date. And as mentioned earlier, final manufacturing design, approvals, and product testing are often negotiated as the responsibility of the licensor.

Improving on your existing licensed patents is a good strategy for extending your royalty income beyond the life of the original patent.

If you are not known in the field where your invention lies, then the best method of placing a license is to identify the companies it will benefit the most and contact them directly. Some will have standard methods for receiving proposals for patents; some will just require persistence to get in the door and tell your story.

There are legitimate brokers out there that will market your patent for you, but there are also a lot of useless services that just want your money and won't deliver results. I have not taken the route of representation, so I can't yet guide you on where to turn for this. I believe contacting companies directly will eventually provide the opening you need.

You want to choose your licensing partners carefully based on their ability to get product to market and their efforts to make sales that will pay you for the term of your agreement. Your license agreement should have clauses that allow you to take back your license rights if certain things are not done and if specified levels of sales are not achieved. As an example, for years now I have received a monthly check for royalty sales on the small appliance vent described earlier. Initially there was one vent we licensed to a small manufacturer and distributor. We later added a second patent on converting the vent to accommodate different appliances by interchanging air-capture shapes. With this, application of the product tripled and the royalty grew accordingly. As time passed, customers requested different sizes and features to fit their particular needs; this increased the product's usefulness further, increasing sales and royalties. Licensing can be a very lucrative way to commercialize your invention.

As a historic reference, the Wright brothers never manufactured airplanes. Once they had achieved notoriety, proved their inventive concepts, and secured patent protection, they licensed rights to manufacture airplanes to a start-up company. They received $100,000 cash (value of over $2 million in today's dollars), one third of the company's stock, and a 10 percent royalty on every plane built. The new company took on the risk of start-up and agreed to cover expenses of infringement suits and other business risks.

To find potential candidates in your field, research companies that have compatible product and, even more importantly, the target market your invention is aimed at. Trade shows, again, are a good vehicle to weigh multiple companies against one another. If any are public companies, you can find a lot of information with web-based stock programs, including brokerage firms like Charles Schwab. By visiting companies' websites, you can often find out their markets, products, and even particular customers in some cases. If you end up with more than one interested party, solicit competitive proposals. Ask each proposal company to project what effort and investment they will put into your product and what their sales projections are. They may balk at this at first, but they should know the market and can estimate their potential sales and returns or they wouldn't be interested.

On a couple of occasions, we had success licensing our inventions when we created a private showing in a hotel suite during a major trade show. We would invite a few known guests and would add to the list while walking around the show talking to executives of the represented companies. We were careful not to have guests come to the suite during trade show hours; this irritates the show sponsors and sometimes your target accounts, because they are there to sell. But a breakfast meeting or a snack and wine visit after the show worked well. We tried both small group showings and single manufacturer showings and the single showing worked best (making sure to let the parties know others were looking). The second approach limits how many you can invite, but provides for serious one-on-one discussions that could close a deal and you only need one deal to start.

We grew this approach into a sanctioned off-site "showcase" of yet to reach the market products, which we ran for several years. It became a "must visit" event for a small group of movers and shakers in our industry comprising potential licensees, interested customers (which interested licensees), design consultants, and the trade press.

Another approach a friend of ours took was to equip a van with his prototype and sales material, then he drove state to state to multiple manufacturers. On their home turf, the manufacturers are generally willing to take a look and talk about what you have available. It's hard to turn down a showing of something unique that might be important to your business, sitting right outside in your parking lot.

As mentioned earlier, your patent may have more than one product application, which then allows for licensing individual products to multiple companies. Another way a single patent is licensed to more than one party is by territory or country (provided you filed for international coverage).

Your commercial lawyer is your best guide on terms of your agreement; however, I have found that certain conditions are beneficial, including a penalty for not getting a product to market by a certain date and having increasing minimum quantities for sales with an annual review. There should be a clause about improvements to your patent or the products you are licensing: improvements should belong to you, the patent holder, regardless of who comes up with the improvement. Improvements that can result in the issuing of a new independent patent can open the door for an extended term to your royalty agreement. The agreements are usually limited to the amount of time remaining on the patent covering the product. If you have an independent improvement that is awarded its own patent, it can extend the time you receive royalties to the expiration of the newer patent; this can be a very lucrative way to keep revenue coming in as your patents age. After you have a successful licensee, you will get to know the company and their products a lot better. Look for other opportunities to create something new for existing clients; it's a lot easier than finding a new party to deal with.

I have included an example licensing agreement in Appendix C; remember each one is different based on negotiations, but it is useful to become familiar with the form and format of such agreements.

The amount of royalty you can charge is dependent on several things: How valuable is your invention to the licensee? How much will they earn from it? What will it do for their business? What is its margin and cost of sales? Royalties range greatly depending on the industry, profit margins on your invention's products, how long the market will last, how much the licensee has to spend to get a product to market. Just remember, you own it, and if you are at the point of talking terms, they want it. I believe in being reasonable, but you deserve the largest royalty for the longest time possible for the inventive effort you invested and the work you put in to finish your creation.

When discussing value with a potential licensee, consider if your product will increase sales of other products the licensee sells or if it will enhance the manufacturer's image in the innovation category of their industry; both are value considerations in a license term.

I have had several licensed patents with years remaining on the agreement when my licensee decided to sell their business. This can be good or bad depending on your considerations. Most acquirers do not want to assume licenses, so they will typically demand an escalation of your license agreement payout. They may offer the full-term royalty based on an estimate of what the sales volume would grow into, discounted to a current value, or they may try to buy you out for a fixed fee. If this is covered in your agreement with the original licensee, then it's a matter of execution and can be much less complicated, so it's wise to consider a sell-out clause when you negotiate the original contract. Getting the cash can be a good thing, but it means full taxes in the year you are paid (but you have the cash now). Your product may grow to higher volumes than calculated and you'd miss some royalty. On the other hand, the buyer may not properly advance your product and you would lose out. Factor these considerations into negotiations.

## PARTNERING (A HYBRID)

One of the most successful methods of commercialization I have used results in a partnering arrangement with very trusted clients. In these cases, we have performed the foundation work for a technology or product and have pending or issued patents and we have a good understanding of whose product line they will be beneficial to. We know the market and the potential of our products.

We approach our intended partners to assess their interest in commercializing these patents. Together with these partners, we have formed new business partnerships, usually as a subsidiary of their normal business. A new co-owned entity is formed with our company contributing the patents as investment and the partner entity paying the costs of completing product development, product testing, and acquiring approvals and full commercialization costs. We maintain a royalty arrangement, and we have an appreciating value in the business entity at a future time based on its appraised valuation. In this way we have a revenue stream, we are involved in continued development to expand the product line, and we have an equity buyout at a point in the future. It combines the best financial possibilities of creating a business and licensing with less risk. Typically we negotiate a potential buyout after five years (or we can opt to stay longer), and we determine a formula for establishing the enterprise value of the product line in the original contract. The royalty may remain after a buyout or can be escalated into present value, also spelled out in the original contract.

In these cases, enterprise value is the business value generated by the product (or product line) in the marketplace based on the current method and multiple of earnings common to the industry you are in. This is a separate value from that of the royalty stream.

When there are partners you can trust, this is my preferred method of doing business; you mitigate a lot of the risks of starting a business on your own yet still benefit from appreciated value that your inventions create and each partner becomes an ongoing client.

Your agreement becomes one of a partnership or LLC corporation, which includes reimbursed costs, royalty schedules, and a formula for a buyout valuation. You are creating a new business subsidy, so it has to include all the typical components of a business partnership. It's best to have legal counsel of both parties cooperate on the partnering agreement.

## INVENTING AS A BUSINESS

If you are a prolific inventor, there is yet another method to capitalize on your inventions: form an invention business where the product of daily activities is inventing. Much like an engineering firm or design firm, you and your team execute all the steps to create new product and collect fees or make license or partnership deals based on the products. It helps to have a couple successful projects under your belt before hanging the shingle.

As you grow, you can add employees with different talents and expand the markets you service. This was our model when we formed Ideas Well Done. In some cases, you invent and develop products for others for a straight fee; this pays the overhead. In other instances, you are paid fees to design and build products based on patents you own, negotiating a fee and a royalty arrangement when a party is interested in what you own. Partnerships as described in the previous section where you own part of the future value created by a third party taking your product to market and an ongoing royalty stream can also be a part of this business. Over time you can build a lucrative fee- and royalty-based business with appreciating ownership positions in the partnership entities. When executed fully, this can be a road to real wealth from your invention talents.

This approach typically would develop after your early success in licensing a patent or two, developing some lasting relationships with your license partners. Soon your client list will grow, you can add disciplines that extend your capabilities for clients, and growth can come from new clients and also from more lucrative deals like partnerships. Start slow and build; it becomes a business of known and trusted partners over time.

Whatever approach you take, your patent(s) can provide you with a long and prosperous career, or if you choose, simply a great income without the daily involvement of running a business. Your choice should be based on your personal assessment of what you enjoy and what you can do best.

I wish you the greatest of luck and immeasurable success and satisfaction. Please stay in touch through my website, Inventing Pathways (https://inventingpathways.com). I would like to write about your success someday. My personal contact is mcolburn.inventingpathways@gmail.com.

Best wishes,
Mike

# Discussion on Profiles

**IN THE "KERNEL OF INVENTION"** profiles throughout this book, I consulted multiple sources for each where they were available and I made every attempt to use my own voice to convey, interpret, and detail the material presented to you. However, I relied heavily on several references that I wish to acknowledge. Each is in the bibliography but deserves to be mentioned and recognized here as sources of extraordinary value to those studying invention or the profiled individuals.

For Leo H Baekeland, *They Made America* by Harold Evans was my primary reference and was a valuable reference throughout the writing of this book. For George Westinghouse, Quentin R. Skrabec Jr.'s biography *George Westinghouse: Gentle Genius* was my primary reference. For Alexander Graham Bell, my primary reference was Charlotte Gray's *Reluctant Genius*. Simon Garfield's history of Sir William Perkin served as my primary source through his book *Mauve*, and finally, except for a visit to the Dr. John Gorrie museum in Apalachicola and some internet references, the only documentation I know of on Dr. John Gorrie is V. M. Sherlock's out-of-print book, *The Fever Man*; a few copies are available at rare book sites.

• APPENDIX A •

# Basic Research

**THERE ARE MANY** sources of information that can assist in your inventive effort. Most universities and many medical institutions have research specialists who often will take on freelance assignments. Of course, there are public libraries and researchers there that can help you as well. However, my experience has been that, in the early days of an inventive project, we learn more by doing the research ourselves. Consider it a mystery to be solved; the answer is out there and you need the clues to find it.

What has served me the best once I have a concrete concept of the problem I intend to solve is to conduct a detailed search of the related "prior art" with some connection to my current problem.

This begins with searching current issued patents as well as US and foreign published patent applications. All are accessible through the US patent office website (https://www.uspto.gov).

When you hear of or read about patent searching, it is usually referencing the process of comparing your invention details with other issued patents and patent applications in order to avoid duplicating what someone has already done, or to avoid entering a situation where you may infringe on someone else's intellectual property. Part of your effort here is to avoid an "obviousness" rejection by a patent examiner. These searches are often late in your inventive process and are necessary and very valuable.

However, I find that doing patent searches early when only the problem is defined will aid in the creation of a worthwhile inventive solution. It stimulates ideas, helps you understand the problem better because of the histories written into patent applications, helps you avoid duplicating time-consuming and expensive experimentation that is already published, and can spark your creativity through thorough investigation.

A well-researched problem concept beginning with patent searches leads to a wealth of knowledge and information to aid your inventive effort. When you locate pertinent patents be sure to study the references cited, foreign patent documents, and other publications listed on the first couple of pages of the patent. These patents and publications, research papers, and other documents are all pertinent to the patent on which they are published and can often contain a wealth of needed knowledge.

What I recommend is to develop an understanding of how to quickly conduct patent searches through the US Patent and Trademark Office (USPTO) and to make it part of your development process from the very beginning when you have fixed on the problem you intend to solve. Review this research again, conducting deeper investigations when you explore solutions.

Most novice researchers fall into the trap of just searching keywords to locate patents or applications that are related to the work they are doing; this is a mistake. A keyword search can be valuable, but you should begin by conducting a classification search, which narrows your findings to more closely resemble your problem.

Beginning in 2013, the USPTO began using a new classification system codeveloped with the European Patent Office, called Cooperative Patent Classification (CPC). It replaces the US Patent Classification (USPC) system and is now exclusive for utility patents. You will still see references to USPC classifications as you do your research, but it is best to learn and use the CPC methods.

To study and practice the seven-step CPC research process, visit the Tutorial section at the USPTO website (https://www.uspto.gov/video/cbt/ptrcsearching/).

You may also visit one of the Patent and Trademark Resource Centers and patent libraries located nationwide where you can get individual help learning how to conduct a thorough search and to get individual input to questions about your project. You can find a location in your state at https://www.uspto.gov/learning-and-resources/support-centers/patent-and-trademark-resource-centers-ptrc/ptrc-locations. It is advisable to call ahead for times and appointments and in some cases to find out if a fee is required.

Before beginning your searches or visiting a resource center, again review your problem statement to see if it is up to date. Depending on your stage of development, write answers to the following list in your notebook; they will serve to provide the guidelines to formulate your search. If your development is in the early stage and you don't have specific answers, create assumed answers and work from there. This list comes directly from the patent search tutorial referenced on the previous page.

1. What is the purpose of your invention?
2. Is the invention a process? Is it a way of making something or performing a function? Or is it product?
3. What is the invention made of? What is the physical composition of the invention?
4. How is the invention used?
5. List keywords or technical terms that describe the nature of the invention.

• APPENDIX B •

# Recommended Reading

There are countless books that could be useful to your inventing efforts; these are just a few of those that I favor and have benefited from.

## Books on Inventing and Inventors

*Thomas Alva Edison: Inventing the Electric Age* by Gene Adair
*Tesla: Inventor of the Electrical Age* by W. Bernard Carlson
*They Made America: From the Steam Engine to the Search Engine: Two Centuries of Innovators* by Harold Evans with Gail Buckland and David Lefer
*Mauve: How One Man Invented a Color That Changed the World* by Simon Garfield
*The Idea Factory: Bell Labs and the Great Age of American Innovation* by Jon Gertner
*Reluctant Genius: Alexander Graham Bell and the Passion for Invention* by Charlotte Gray
*Alexander Graham Bell: The Spirit of Innovation* by Jennifer Groundwater
*Code Name Ginger: The Story Behind Segway and Dean Kamen's Quest to Invent a New World* by Steve Kemper
*The Boy Who Invented TV: The Story of Philo Farnsworth* by Kathleen Krull
*Inventing Joy* by Joy Mangano with Alex Tresniowski
*Edison and the Business of Innovation* by Andre Millard
*Thomas A. Edison and the Menlo Park Experience: Working at Inventing* edited by William S. Pretzer

*Juice: The Creative Fuel That Drives World-Class Inventors* by Evan I. Schwartz

*The Last Lone Inventor: A Tale of Genius, Deceit, and the Birth of Television* by Evan I. Schwartz

*George Westinghouse: Gentle Genius* by Quentin R. Skrabec Jr.

*American Science and Invention: A Pictorial History* by Mitchell Wilson

## Books on Philosophy, Creativity, and Technique

*As a Man Thinketh* by James Allen

*Inventive Engineering: Knowledge and Skills for Creative Engineers* by Tomasz Arciszewski

*Making Ideas Happen: Overcoming the Obstacles Between Vision and Reality* by Scott Belsky

*How to Mind Map: Make the Most of Your Mind and Learn How to Create, Organize, and Plan* by Tony Buzan

*Sherlock Holmes: The Complete Novels and Stories* by Sir Arthur Conan Doyle, with introduction by Loren D. Estleman

*Drawing on the Right Side of the Brain: A Course in Enhancing Creativity and Artistic Confidence* by Betty Edwards

*How to Get Ideas* by Jack Foster

*How to Think Like Leonardo da Vinci: Seven Steps to Genius Every Day* by Michael J. Gelb

*Think and Grow Rich* by Napoleon Hill, and revised and expanded by Dr. Arthur R. Pell

*Where Good Ideas Come From: The Natural History of Innovation* by Steven Johnson

*The Art of Innovation: Lessons in Creativity from IDEO, America's Leading Design Firm* by Tom Kelley with Jonathan Littman

*The Power of Your Subconscious Mind* by Joseph Murphy, PhD, DD

*A Whole New Mind: Moving from the Information Age to the Conceptual Age* by Daniel H. Pink

*If . . . : A Mind-Bending New Way of Looking at Big Ideas and Numbers* by David J. Smith

*The Creative Habit: Learn It and Use It for Life* by Twyla Tharp with Mark Reiter

*A Technique for Producing Ideas* by James Webb Young

## Books on Marketing and Licensing Your Invention

*The Inventor's Bible: How to Market and License Your Brilliant Ideas* by Ronald Louis Docie Sr.

*Invent It, Sell It, Bank It!: Make Your Million-Dollar Idea into a Reality* by Lori Greiner

*One Simple Idea: Turn Your Dreams into a Licensing Goldmine While Letting Others Do the Work* by Stephen Key

*The Mom Inventors Handbook: How to Turn Your Great Idea into the Next Big Thing* by Tamara Monosoff

# Sample Forms

The following forms are intended as samples and each can take on varying terms and conditions. If you choose to use any version, do so at your own risk. It is always advisable to have your legal counsel review any legal document before agreeing to its terms and conditions.

## Noncompete and Nondisclosure Forms

This form should be used when hiring an employee, or it can be modified when hiring a contractor to work on your projects. If you are not working with a company name, substitute your own.

### AGREEMENT ON INVENTIONS AND PATENTS

Agreement made between _____________ (Company) and ______________ (Employee/Contractor) this ____ day of ________, 20__. In consideration of the employment (engagement) or continued employment of Employee by Company, the parties agree to the following:

1. Employee (contractor) may have access to apparatus, equipment, drawings, reports, manuals, inventions, customer lists, computer programs, or other trade secrets or confidential, technical, or business information of Company or its Affiliates. Employee (contractor) therein agrees

   (a) not to use any such trade secrets, inventions, information, or material hereto for himself or others, and

   (b) not to remove any such items or reproductions from Company facilities, either during or after employment by Company, except as absolutely required in Employee's (contractors) duties to Company upon request, and in any event upon termination of employment (engagement).

2. Employee (contractor) agrees not to disclose or publish any trade secret or confidential technical or business information of Company or its Affiliates or of another party to whom Company owes an obligation of confidentiality, either during or after employment of Company, without authorization of Company.

3. Employee (contractor) shall promptly provide Company a complete record of any and all inventions and improvements, whether patentable or not, which Employee (contractor), solely or jointly, may conceive, make or first disclose during said employment (engagement).

4. Employee (contractor) hereby grants, assigns, and delivers to Company, or its nominee, Employee's (contractor's) entire right, title, and interest in and to all improvements coming within the scope of Paragraph 3 that relate in any way to actual or anticipated business or activities of Company, or its Affiliates, or that are suggested by or result from any task or work for or on behalf of Company or its Affiliates, together with any and all domestic and foreign patent rights in such inventions and improvements. To assist Company or its nominee in securing patents thereto, both during and after employment, without additional compensation but at Company's expense.

5. Employee (contractor) agrees that, upon accepting employment (engagement) with any organization in competition with Company or its Affiliates during a period of one year(s) following employment termination, Employee shall notify Company in writing within thirty days of the name and address of such new employer.

6. Employee (contractor) agrees to give Company timely written notice of any prior employment agreements or patent rights that may conflict within the interests of Company or its Affiliates.

7. No waiver by either party of any breach by the other party of any provision of this Agreement shall be deemed or construed to be a waiver of a later breach of such provision.

8. This Agreement shall be binding upon the inure to the benefit of the parties and their successors and assigns.

9. Where inconsistent, this Agreement supersedes the terms of any prior employment agreement or understanding between employee (contractor) and Company. This Agreement may be modified or amended only in writing, duly signed by Company and Employee (contractor).

10. It is agreed that this Agreement will be interrupted and construed according to the laws of the state where Company is located. Should any portion of this Agreement be judicially held to be invalid, unenforceable or void, then such holding shall not invalidate the remainder of this Agreement or any other part thereof.

*Employee (contractor) acknowledges reading, understanding, and receiving a signed copy of this Agreement.*

| | |
|---|---|
| Your Business or Name | Employee/Contractor Name |
| Date | Date |
| Company Officer Signature | Employee's (Contractor's) Signature |

Use this form for disclosing confidential information that you want to protect from release to any unauthorized party and to protect your potential patent rights. You can substitute a company name or your name for "owner" when appropriate. You can also substitute your state for "Vermont" in paragraph 8. There can be many variations of this type of agreement; modify it to your needs.

**NONDISCLOSURE AGREEMENT**

This Nondisclosure Agreement (the "Agreement"), dated as of the ___ day of ____________, 20___, is by and between _______________ (the "Owner"), with an address of ______________________________, and (the "Recipient"), with an address of ______________________________________________.

(Name and Address)

To induce the Owner to provide Recipient with certain information that is proprietary and/or confidential, Recipient agrees to the following terms and conditions:

1. Business Relationship. In the course of Recipient's business relationship with Owner, Recipient may learn, or may have access to, certain proprietary and/or confidential information belonging to Owner ("Confidential Information").

2. Definition of Confidential Information. As used throughout this Agreement, Confidential Information means any proprietary, secret, confidential, or other similar information relating to Owner's business. This information may include, but is not limited to, prototypes, product development techniques and plans, manufacturing and assembly processes, technical processes, inventions, designs, product materials, product test data, trade "know-how," trade secrets, marketing plans and strategies, financial statements and projections, and customer lists. Confidential Information does not include information which is generally known to the trade or to the public at the time of disclosure.

3. Nondisclosure. Recipient agrees that Recipient will keep strictly confidential all Confidential Information, and will not (except as required by applicable law, regulation, or legal process) without prior written consent of Owner, signed by one of Owner's authorized officers, use, disclose, sell, or market any Confidential Information to any third person, firm, corporation, or association for any purpose. Recipient further agrees that Recipient will not make any copies of the Confidential Information except upon Owner's written authorization, signed by one of Owner's authorized officers, and

will not remove any copy or sample of Confidential Information from the premises of Owner without such authorization.

4. Return of Confidential Information. Upon receipt of a written request from Owner, Recipient will return to Owner all copies or samples of Confidential Information that, at the time of the receipt of the notice, are in Recipient's possession.

5. Obligations Continue. The obligations imposed on Recipient shall continue with respect to the Confidential Information following termination of the business relationship between Recipient and Owner, and such obligations shall not terminate until any Confidential Information shall cease to be secret and confidential and shall be in the public domain.

6. Severability. If any provision of this Agreement or its application is held to be invalid, illegal, or unenforceable in any respect, the validity, legality, or enforceability of any of the other provisions and applications therein shall not in any way be affected or impaired.

7. Entire Agreement. This Agreement sets forth the entire understanding between the Recipient and the Owner with respect to Confidential Information and may not be modified, changed, or amended, except by a writing signed by the party to be charged.

8. Controlling Law. This Agreement, regardless of where made, shall be construed and enforced in accordance with Vermont law.

*Dated as of the date above first written.*

Owner

By: ______________________________________________

Its Duly Authorized Agent

Recipient

By: ______________________________________________

Its Duly Authorized Agent

This form is used when there is a chance that both parties will disclose confidential information to the other. Substitute your state for "Vermont" in jurisdiction statements. Substitute your company or name for "company."

## MUTUAL CONFIDENTIALITY AGREEMENT

This Mutual Confidentiality Agreement is entered into effect the ____ day of __________, 20____, by and between ____________________________, the principal place of business of which is ______________________________ and Company (you), the principal place of business of which is located at ______________________________ (hereinafter called "Company").

**WITNESSETH**

WHEREAS, each of the parties hereto considers that all of the nonpublic information, ideas, formulae, technical data, financial information, employee benefit plans, supplier, customer, and distributor identities and arrangements, corporate practices, procedures, and other data owned or used by it, which, together with all photographs, copies, reproductions, extractions, tracings, outlines, paraphrasing, bulletins, memoranda, manuals, records, summaries, letters, books, and notes in which the same may be embodied (hereinafter collectively referred to as "Proprietary information"), is confidential and its sole property, and

WHEREAS, it is to the mutual benefit of the parties hereto to disclose, each to the other, certain Proprietary Information and to permit the other to make photocopies, outlines, summaries, and memoranda thereof,

NOW, THEREFORE, in consideration of the mutual benefits to be derived therefrom and the disclosures made and to be made by the parties hereto, each to the other, the parties hereto agree as follows:

1. Each of the parties hereto shall deliver and disclose certain of its Proprietary Information to the other for the purpose of collaboration between ______________________________ and Company.

2. All Proprietary Information disclosed hereunder shall be and remains exclusively the property of the disclosing party and shall be held in the strictest confidence by the other party. No Proprietary Information may be disclosed or delivered to others or used by the party receiving it for any purpose (other than the limited purpose described in Section 1 of this Agreement) without the prior written consent of the party making such disclosure.

3. Except as necessary for the performance of the services contemplated by this Agreement or as expressly authorized in writing by the party disclosing such Proprietary Information, the party receiving it agrees that such party will not copy, take notes of, photograph, outline, summarize, reproduce in any way, disclose or use the Proprietary Information or any part thereof and that such party will return to the disclosing party, upon the disclosing party's request, all documents provided by the disclosing party and all copies, summaries, notes, and outlines thereof.

4. Each party hereto shall take reasonable measures to prevent unauthorized disclosure of Proprietary Information.

5. The obligations set forth in this Agreement shall not apply to:

    a. Information which is in the public domain as of the date of this Agreement or which later comes into the public domain from a source other than the party hereto receiving it pursuant to this Agreement; and

    b. Information approved for release by written authorization of the party disclosing it hereunder.

6. The provisions of this Agreement shall be construed as agreements which are independent of any other agreement between the parties, hereto and the existence of any claim or cause of action by either of them against the other, whether predicated on this or any other agreement, shall not constitute a defense or offset to the enforcement of the covenants contained in this Agreement.

7. This Agreement shall be construed and enforced in accordance with the laws of the State of _______ and the interpretation, application and enforcement of this Agreement shall be governed by the laws of that State, but without regard to such laws as may rely upon or refer to the laws of any other jurisdiction in the resolution of conflicts of law or for other purposes. The terms and conditions of this Agreement shall prevail over and supersede any contrary or conflicting provisions of the Uniform Trade Secrets Act, including the version thereof enacted in _________ and in effect from time to time, to the extent that any such provision may be applicable to any matter or transaction governed or contemplated by this Agreement. If either party to this Agreement breaches or defaults in the performance of any of its covenants or violates any applicable restrictions, a judgment of damages awarded to the other party would not be adequate relief, and the other party may, if it so elects, enforce its rights under this Agreement by obtaining a restraining order and injunction against any further breaches or defaults by the other party, as well as recovering damages.

8. Any dispute arising under this Agreement that is not settled by Agreement between the parties to this Agreement shall be subject to resolution only by appropriate legal proceedings in the Superior Court of Vermont or

the United States District Court for the District of _______________. ____________________________ and company agree that any proceeding instituted in either of such courts shall be of proper venue, that such court shall have personal jurisdiction of the parties, and that any and all pleadings, summons, motions, and other process in such proceeding shall be fully and effectively served when transmitted by United States mail (registered or certified, if mailed within the United States) postage and registry fees prepaid. Pending any decision, appeal of judgment in such proceeding, or the settlement of any dispute arising under this Agreement, __________________________ and all other persons receiving Proprietary Information from _________________________ shall perform, observe, and comply with all covenants, conditions, and other terms of this Agreement required of ____________________________ and such other persons.

**IN WITNESS WHEREOF,** _____________________ and company have entered into this Mutual Confidentiality Agreement on the day and year first above written.

| Company | Second Party |
|---|---|
| By: ___________________________ | By: ___________________________ |
| (Printed Name)<br>(And Title) | (Printed Name)<br>(And Title) |
| Signature: ______________________ | Signature: ______________________ |

## Licensing Agreement

A license and use agreement can take on many different forms with terms and conditions particular to the individual deal. This form is just to give you an example. I would not recommend using this form without consulting with a business-oriented lawyer to negotiate the intricate details of your deal.

### PATENT AND PRODUCT LICENSE AGREEMENT

This license agreement ("AGREEMENT"), effective _______, 20__ ("EFFECTIVE DATE") is by and between (your company), and its AFFILIATES, a company organized and existing under the laws of (your State), having its principal place of business at (your address)(hereinafter, together with its AFFILIATES, referred to as "LICENSOR") and __________________ Inc., a _________ organized and existing under the laws of _________, having its principal place of business at __________________________ (hereinafter, together with its AFFILIATES, referred to as "LICENSEE") (individually a "PARTY" or collectively the "PARTIES"), who agree as follows:

1. **Background**

   **1.1** LICENSOR with its AFFILIATES is the owner of the entire right, title, and interest to certain patent rights relating to (general topic of your invention).

   **1.2** LICENSEE is interested in acquiring for itself a license as set forth in this AGREEMENT to use certain LICENSOR patent rights and product concepts and designs for its benefit and for the benefit of its customers and end consumers.

   **1.3** LICENSOR is willing to grant such a license, under the terms and conditions set forth in this AGREEMENT.

2. **Definitions**

   **2.1 General.** The capitalized terms defined herein shall have the meanings indicated for purposes of this AGREEMENT; noncapitalized terms have their common meaning.

   **2.2 "AFFILIATES"** means any partnership, joint venture, corporation, or other legal entity controlling, controlled by, or under common control with LICENSOR or LICENSEE, respectively, through stock ownership or other equity interest, direct or indirect.

   **2.3 "IMPROVEMENTS"** means all developments, enhancements, or advancements made to the LICENSED PRODUCTS developed by either PARTY during the TERM of this AGREEMENT (including all related technical ideas, discoveries, drawings, inventions, know-how, and formulation technology), whether or not such development, enhancement, or advancement is patentable itself, and also includes developments, enhancements, or advancements with respect to components, materials, or processes that are useful in practicing the invention of a patent claim, but do not themselves infringe a patent claim.

**2.4 "LICENSED PRODUCT(S)"** means products as further defined in Schedule A embody one or more VALID CLAIM(s) of LICENSOR PATENT RIGHTS and/or PRODUCT DESIGNS CONDEPTS PROVIDED TO LICENSOR.

**2.5 "LICENSOR PATENT RIGHTS"** means rights related to US Patent Application No. ________________ and US Patent Application No. ________________ and equivalents and foreign counterparts thereof that are owned or controlled by LICENSOR within the TERRITORY, and any continuations, divisional patents, reissues, and reexaminations thereof, and any substitute or related patent rights that LICENSOR may also own or license, which are necessary to enable LICENSEE to enjoy the intent of the rights granted in Section 3.1, each of which and together are a "LICENSOR PATENT."

**2.6 "NET SALES,"** for the purpose of computing royalties, means LICENSEE's (including its AFFILIATES or sublicenses if applicable) gross sales (the gross invoice amount billed customers) of LICENSED PRODUCTS, less excise taxes, discounts, and allowances actually shown on the invoice (except cash discounts that are not deductible in the calculation of royalty) and, further, less any bona fide returns (net of all returns actually made or allowed as supported by credit memoranda actually issued to the customers) up to the amount of the actual sales of the LICENSED PRODUCT during the royalty period. No other costs incurred in the manufacturing, selling, advertising, and distribution of the LICENSED PRODUCTS will be deducted nor will any deduction be allowed for any uncollectible accounts or allowances. If LICENSEE sells any LICENSED PRODUCT to a LICENSEE AFFILIATE, the royalty will be calculated on the regular price.

**2.7 "MARKET"** means the retail market.

**2.8 "PERSON"** means (as the context requires) an individual, a corporation, a partnership, an association, a trust, a limited liability company, or other entity or organization, including a governmental entity.

**2.9 "TERM"** means the life of LICENSORS PATENTS, unless this AGREEMENT is earlier terminated as further provided below.

**2.10 "TERRITORY"** means worldwide.

**2.11 "THIRD PARTY"** means any PERSON that is not a PARTY or AFFILIATE of a PARTY.

**2.12 "VALID CLAIM"** means any patent claim in an unexpired patent or pending patent application included within LICENSOR PATENT RIGHTS that has not been disclaimed, abandoned, or held invalid or unenforceable by a decision beyond the right of review, such as by a court of last resort from which no further appeal can be taken or by a governmental body with the authority to determine the patentability, validity, or enforceability of patent claims.

3. License Grant

**3.1 License to LICENSOR PATENT RIGHTS.** LICENSOR grants to LICENSEE, subject to all the terms and conditions of this AGREEMENT, a non-exclusive license in the LICENSED PATENTS during the TERM for the exclusive right to make, use, and sell the systems and methods embodying the invention(s) described in the LICENSOR PATENTS for ____________ (product) for the MARKET in the TERRITORY as and for LICENSED PRODUCTS.

This LICENSE includes the non-exclusive right of LICENSEE to exploit LICENSOR'S trade secret technologies as may be communicated to LICENSEE from time to time as such are essential to enable LICENSEE'S exclusive right to enjoy the LICENSOR PATENT RIGHTS with respect to LICENSED PRODUCT in the MARKET in the TERRITORY. All LICENSOR trade secret technology is LICENSOR CONFIDENTIAL INFORMATION.

This LICENSE includes the right of LICENSEE to sub-license its rights as granted by this AGREEMENT to its contract manufacturers of LICENSED PRODUCT and LICENSED PRODUCT parts, provided that LICENSOR be informed of the identity of each contract manufacturer in each instance, that LICENSEE confirms to LICENSOR that each contractor is bound in writing to the obligations and restrictions of this AGREEMENT as to LICENSOR'S PATENTS and LICENSEE CONFIDENTIAL INFORMATION, that each sublicense(s) terminate no later than with this AGREEMENT and that LICENSEE is liable to LICENSOR for any breach by its sub-licensees of such rights.



**3.2 No Other Licenses Granted.** The licenses granted under this

AGREEMENT are limited to those specifically set forth in Paragraph **3.1** (entitled "License to LICENSOR PATENT RIGHTS") and under this AGREEMENT no license is granted under any other patents or technology now or hereafter owned by LICENSOR, except for any divisional, continuation, or substitute US patent applications based on LICENSOR PATENTS, and any patents that issue on any of the above-described patent applications or on any IMPROVEMENTS, and any reissues and extensions thereof now or hereafter owned by LICENSOR as such relate directly to steam generating technology as used in LICENSED PRODUCT in the MARKET in the TERRITORY and essential to enable LICENSEE to enjoy the rights granted by this AGREEMENT.

**3.3 Reservation of Rights.** All rights not expressly granted to LICENSEE by this AGREEMENT are reserved to LICENSOR, including without limitation the right of LICENSOR to make, use, license, or otherwise exploit and sell the systems and methods embodying the invention(s) of the LICENSOR PATENTS with respect to products other than the LICENSED PRODUCTS in the MARKET.

**3.4 Marking.** All LICENSED PRODUCT and LICENSED PRODUCT packaging will bear appropriate patent notices as provided by LICENSOR to LICENSEE from time to time.

**4. Payments, Reports, and Records**

As consideration for the rights and licenses granted herein, LICENSEE shall pay LICENSOR in the manner and upon conditions set forth in this Section:

**4.1 Royalty.** LICENSEE shall pay royalties to LICENSOR at a rate of _____ percent (__%) of the NET SALES of LICENSED PRODUCTS.

During each calendar year during the TERM of this AGREEMENT, LICENSEE agrees to pay LICENSOR a "Guaranteed Minimum Royalty" as provided in Schedule A which will be credited against LICENSEE'S actual royalty obligation to LICENSOR. The Guaranteed Minimum Royalty will be calculated at the end of each calendar year. In the event that LICENSEE's actual Royalties paid LICENSOR for any calendar year are less than the Guaranteed Minimum Royalty for such year, LICENSEE will, in addition to paying LICENSOR its actual earned royalty for such royalty period, pay LICENSOR the difference between the total earned Royalty for the year and the Guaranteed Minimum Royalty for such year. The Guaranteed Minimum Royalty will be pro-rated for any partial calendar year during the TERM.

A royalty obligation will accrue on the sale of the LICENSED PRODUCTS regardless of the time of collection by LICENSEE. A LICENSED PRODUCT is considered "sold" when such LICENSED PRODUCT is billed, invoiced, shipped, or paid for, whichever occurs first.

Acceptance of any royalty payment by LICENSOR will not prevent LICENSOR from challenging the validity or accuracy of any royalty report or payment. Upon expiration or termination of this AGREEMENT for any reason, all royalty obligations, including Guaranteed Minimum Royalties, will immediately be due and payable. Royalty payment obligations accrued during the TERM will survive termination of this AGREEMENT for any reason.

All royalty payments will be calculated and made in US dollars.

Overdue royalties will bear a penalty fee of 1% per month from the date due until paid in full. LICENSOR will be responsible for LICENSEE'S reasonable costs of collection, including attorneys' fees and costs.

**4.2 Payment Due Date.** Any and all royalties payable above shall be paid to LICENSOR within sixty (60) calendar days of the close of each quarter of a calendar year within which the royalties accrued.

**4.3 Statements.** LICENSEE shall prepare and issue reports for each quarter of a calendar year, identifying this AGREEMENT and showing separately:

- **a.** Total number of LICENSED PRODUCTS on a country-by-country basis, the stock number, item, units sold, description, quantity shipped, gross invoice, amount billed customers less discounts, allowances, returns, and reportable sales for each LICENSED PRODUCT sold, delivered, provided, or otherwise disposed of by LICENSEE, if applicable.
- **b.** The royalties accrued during the applicable quarter of the calendar year and payable to LICENSOR by LICENSEE.

If no sales, deliveries, or dispositions of LICENSED PRODUCTS were made during a quarter, a report to that effect shall be filed.

**4.4 Audit and Inspection.**

**4.4.1 Records.** LICENSEE shall keep and maintain at its regular place of business books and records of all transactions carried out by LICENSEE in connection with this AGREEMENT, including accounting books and records, sales, shipments, deduction and promotion ledgers, written policies and procedures, and general ledger entries (hereinafter collectively referred to as the "RECORDS").

**4.4.2 Audit.** LICENSEE's RECORDS shall be subject to audit and reproduction by LICENSEE or its authorized agents during the full term of this AGREEMENT and for one (1) year subsequent to the date of expiration or termination, as hereinafter provided. For the purpose of ensuring verification of compliance by LICENSEE with all requirements of this AGREEMENT, LICENSOR shall have the right to inspect and audit the RECORDS during regular business hours, provided that LICENSOR shall give to LICENSEE at least ten (10) business days advance written notice of its intention to do so. All overdue royalty payments as disclosed by the audit, plus accrued penalties thereon, will be immediately due and payable. In the event the audit discloses an underpayment of three (3%) percent or more, LICENSEE will be responsible for LICENSOR'S reasonable costs of audit.

**4.5 Taxes and Governmental Approvals.** LICENSEE will be solely responsible for the payment of any and all taxes, fees, duties, and other payments incurred in relation to the manufacture, use, import, export, and sale of LICENSED PRODUCTS. LICENSEE will be solely responsible for applying for and obtaining at its own expense any approvals, authorizations, or validations necessary to effectuate the terms of this AGREEMENT under the laws of the appropriate national laws of each of the countries in the TERRITORY.

**5. Patent Maintenance Fees**

**5.1 Maintenance Fees.** LICENSOR will pay all patent maintenance fees and/or annuity fees for any patent or patent application covered by this AGREEMENT. LICENSOR may abandon any patent or patent application covered by this AGREEMENT provided that, at least ninety (90) days prior to such abandonment, LICENSOR shall inform LICENSEE in writing of its intention to abandon to determine if LICENSEE wishes to be assigned such patent or patent application. The terms of any assignment of any patent or patent application covered by this AGREEMENT from LICENSOR to LICENSEE shall be set forth in a separate agreement. Upon assignment, LICENSEE shall be responsible for payment of any maintenance and/or annuity fees.

**6. Confidentiality**

**6.1 Disclosure of CONFIDENTIAL INFORMATION.** During the term of this AGREEMENT, it may be necessary for a PARTY ("DISCLOSING PARTY") to disclose to the other PARTY ("RECEIVING PARTY"), orally or in writing, technical and business information relating to LICENSOR PATENT RIGHTS, LICENSED PRODUCTS, or a PARTY's business operations or customers, which the DISCLOSING PARTY considers confidential ("CONFIDENTIAL INFORMATION"), for purposes of carrying out the PARTIES' respective obligations under this AGREEMENT.

**6.1.1 Obligation of Confidentiality.** The DISCLOSING PARTY agrees to disclose CONFIDENTIAL INFORMATION to the RECEIVING PARTY upon the following conditions which are understood to be acceptable to both PARTIES:

**a.** The CONFIDENTIAL INFORMATION will be received and held in confidence by the RECEIVING PARTY.

**b.** The RECEIVING PARTY will take such steps as may be reasonably necessary to prevent the disclosure of CONFIDENTIAL INFORMATION to any THIRD PARTY.

**c.** The RECEIVING PARTY will not use for its own purposes or commercially utilize CONFIDENTIAL INFORMATION (unless in a manner consistent with this AGREEMENT) without first having obtained the written consent of the DISCLOSING PARTY.

**6.1.2 Limitation.** The commitments set forth in Section 6.1.1 above and all subsections thereof shall not extend to any portion of CONFIDENTIAL INFORMATION:

**a.** which is already in the RECEIVING PARTY's lawful possession at the time of disclosure by the DISCLOSING PARTY, as established by relevant documentary evidence; or

**b.** which is or later becomes, through no act or omission on the part of the RECEIVING PARTY, generally available to the public; or

**c.** which corresponds in substance to that furnished to the RECEIVING PARTY by any THIRD PARTY that to the RECEIVING PARTY's knowledge had no obligation of confidentiality, direct or indirect, to the DISCLOSING PARTY; or

**d.** which corresponds to that furnished by the DISCLOSING PARTY to any THIRD PARTY on a non-confidential basis other than in connection with limited consumer testing; or

**e.** which is independently developed by the RECEIVING PARTY by personnel not aware of the CONFIDENTIAL INFORMATION of the DISCLOSING PARTY, as established by relevant documentary evidence; or

**f.** which is required to be disclosed by law or government regulation provided that the RECEIVING PARTY provides reasonable prior notice when possible of such required disclosure to the DISCLOSING PARTY.

**6.1.3 Form of Disclosure.** The obligations of the RECEIVING PARTY under Section 6.1.1 (entitled "Obligation of Confidentiality") shall extend only to CONFIDENTIAL INFORMATION which is disclosed to the RECEIVING PARTY by the DISCLOSING PARTY:

**a.** in written form and designated as confidential at the time of disclosure; or

**b.** orally or visually and the CONFIDENTIAL INFORMATION is summarized in a written disclosure clearly designated as confidential or its confidentiality is confirmed in writing within thirty (30) calendar days of such oral or visual disclosure of the subject CONFIDENTIAL INFORMATION; or

**c.** which a reasonable person would understand to be confidential, notwithstanding the fact that no designation or written confirmation occurs.

**6.1.4 Return of CONFIDENTIAL INFORMATION.** Upon written request of the DISCLOSING PARTY, the RECEIVING PARTY shall return to the DISCLOSING PARTY all written documentation of CONFIDENTIAL INFORMATION which was received by the RECEIVING PARTY, however, the RECEIVING PARTY shall be permitted to maintain one copy of the written documentation of CONFIDENTIAL INFORMATION in a confidential file maintained by RECEIVING PARTY's counsel for purposes of monitoring compliance with this AGREEMENT.

**6.1.5 Termination of Confidentiality Obligations.** Notwithstanding termination of this AGREEMENT, the obligations of confidentiality and nonuse of the RECEIVING PARTY under this Section 6 with respect to specific portions of CONFIDENTIAL INFORMATION shall survive for a period of five (5) years from the end of the TERM of this AGREEMENT, provided, however, that if the CONFIDENTIAL INFORMATION is trade secret information under the Uniform Trade Secret Act, until such information is no longer a trade secret without it losing its trade secret status by any action or omission of the RECEIVING PARTY.

**6.1.6 No Rights by Implication.** Except as otherwise expressly set forth herein, neither this AGREEMENT nor the disclosure of CONFIDENTIAL INFORMATION hereunder shall be deemed by implication, or otherwise, to vest in the RECEIVING PARTY any present or future rights in any patents, trade secrets, or other property of the DISCLOSING PARTY.

**6.1.7 Disclosure of Other PARTY's CONFIDENTIAL INFORMATION to Employees.** The RECEIVING PARTY may disclose CONFIDENTIAL INFORMATION to its officers, directors, employees, and consultants (if applicable) only to the extent necessary to enable them to comply with or monitor compliance with the terms of this AGREEMENT, provided that the RECEIVING PARTY shall remain responsible for compliance with the terms of this AGREEMENT.

**6.1.8 Additional Exceptions to Obligations of Confidentiality.** Nothing herein shall prevent either PARTY from disclosing CONFIDENTIAL INFORMATION in response to any form of validly issued legal process or investigative demand from a court or government entity of competent jurisdiction calling for the disclosure of such CONFIDENTIAL INFORMATION, provided that, to the extent feasible, the RECEIVING PARTY served with such process or demand gives notice to the DISCLOSING PARTY of the process or demand sufficiently in advance of the requested disclosure to permit either PARTY or both PARTIES to oppose the process or demand, if appropriate, or to seek to condition any such disclosure upon the entry of a suitable agreement or protective order respecting the confidentiality of the CONFIDENTIAL INFORMATION to be disclosed. The DISCLOSING PARTY shall be responsible for the cost of obtaining such a protective order or limitation.

**6.1.9 Terms of AGREEMENT are Confidential.** LICENSEE may disclose the existence of this AGREEMENT to its customers or potential customers in connection with sales of the LICENSED PRODUCTS. However, unless required by applicable law, neither the actual terms of this AGREEMENT nor the AGREEMENT itself shall ever be disclosed to a THIRD PARTY by either LICENSEE or LICENSOR without the prior written consent of the other PARTY.

## 7. Improvements

**7.1** In the event that LICENSOR or LICENSEE develops any IMPROVEMENT in the LICENSOR PATENTS, and later incorporated in an improved or modified LICENSED PRODUCT by LICENSEE, such improved product will be a LICENSED PRODUCT subject to the payment of royalties as otherwise provided in this AGREEMENT. All IMPROVEMENTS made by the LICENSEE will be promptly disclosed to LICENSOR and will thereafter be the property of LICENSOR. LICENSEE hereby acknowledges and agrees that it will, and shall cause its AFFILIATES to, execute or deliver any further instruments, information, explanations, or documents and take all such further action as may be necessary to grant to LICENSOR all right and title in the IMPROVEMENTS and for LICENSOR to fully enjoy all of the rights and benefits to such IMPROVEMENTS, such assistance to be rendered promptly and at no expense, but no compensation, to LICENSEE. This obligation will survive expiration or termination of this AGREEMENT for any reason.

8. **Representations, Warranties, and Disclaimers**

**8.1 Ownership.** LICENSOR represents and warrants that to the best of its knowledge and belief it and its AFFILIATES are the sole and exclusive owner of all right, title, and interest to the LICENSOR PATENT RIGHTS.

**8.2 Authority.** Each PARTY represents and warrants that it has authority to enter into this AGREEMENT and to perform its obligations under this AGREEMENT and that it has been duly authorized to execute and to deliver this AGREEMENT.

**8.3 Freedom-to-Practice.** LICENSOR represents and warrants that it is not aware of any patent rights held by a THIRD PARTY that would hinder the Freedom to Practice of LICENSEE with respect to the LICENSED PRODUCTS contemplated by this AGREEMENT.

9. **Enforcement and Validity Challenged**

**9.1 Notice.** If LICENSOR becomes aware of any potential infringement by a THIRD PARTY of LICENSOR PATENT RIGHTS within the MARKET and within the TERRITORY, it shall notify LICENSEE and shall provide to LICENSEE any information LICENSOR has in support of such belief. If LICENSEE becomes aware of any potential infringement by a THIRD PARTY of LICENSOR PATENT RIGHTS, it shall notify LICENSOR and shall provide to LICENSOR any information LICENSEE has in support of such belief.

**9.2 Enforcement.**

**9.2.1 Enforcement by LICENSEE.** With respect to any potential infringement by a THIRD PARTY of LICENSOR PATENT RIGHTS within the MARKET and within the TERRITORY, LICENSEE may elect to institute any such action and/or legal proceeding as it deems appropriate to enjoin and/or recover damages for the potential infringement of LICENSOR PATENT RIGHTS within the MARKET and within the TERRITORY through negotiation, litigation, and/or alternative dispute resolution means, at LICENSEE's sole cost and expense. LICENSEE shall have the right to select and to control counsel in any action and/or legal proceeding initiated by LICENSEE. If LICENSEE institutes such action and/or legal proceeding, LICENSOR shall lend its name to the action and/or legal proceeding or join as a party in any such action and/or legal proceeding, and provide assistance as may be reasonably necessary to conduct the action and/or legal proceeding. LICENSEE has the right to settle such action and/or legal proceeding at LICENSEE's sole discretion, but shall not in any way restrict or narrow LICENSOR's ownership of the LICENSOR PATENT RIGHTS. LICENSEE shall be entitled to any and all recovery from such enforcement provided that LICENSOR will be entitled to Royalties on the established value of the infringing products as recovered by LICENSEE after payment of LICENSEE'S costs and expenses of suit.

**9.2.2 Enforcement by LICENSOR.** If pursuant to Section 9.2.1 above, LICENSEE elects not to institute such action and/or legal proceeding to enjoin and/or recover damages including past damages for the potential infringement of LICENSOR PATENT RIGHTS within the MARKET and within the TERRITORY, LICENSEE will promptly notify LICENSOR of its election. After receiving notice of LICENSEE's election not to pursue the potential infringement, LICENSOR may institute an action and/or legal proceeding to enjoin and/or recover damages including past damages for such potential infringement at LICENSOR's own cost and expense. LICENSOR shall have the right to select and to control counsel in any action and/or legal proceeding initiated by LICENSOR. LICENSEE shall lend its name to the action and/or legal proceeding or join as a party in any such action and/or legal proceeding, and provide assistance as may be reasonably necessary to conduct the action and/or legal proceeding. LICENSOR has the right to settle such action and/or legal proceeding at LICENSOR's sole discretion, but shall not in any way restrict or narrow LICENSEE's license granted hereunder. LICENSOR shall be entitled to any and all recovery from such enforcement.

**10. Indemnification**

**10.1 Indemnification of LICENSOR.** LICENSEE agrees to indemnify, defend, and hold harmless LICENSOR, its AFFILIATES, and any of their agents, officers, directors, and employees from and against any actual or alleged liability, claim, administrative action, cause of action, suit, damages, and expenses (including reasonable attorney fees and costs) related to any THIRD PARTY claim of damages for personal injuries, including death, and property damage and any other costs of whatsoever nature incurred by LICENSOR arising from the manufacture, use, marketing and sale of LICENSED PRODUCTS.

**10.2 Indemnification of LICENSEE.** LICENSOR agrees to indemnify, defend, and hold harmless LICENSEE, its AFFILIATES, and any of their agents, officers, directors, and employees from and against any actual or alleged liability, claim, administrative action, cause of action, suit, damages, and expenses (including reasonable attorney fees and costs) related to any THIRD PARTY claim of patent infringement and/or misappropriation of trade secrets with respect to the design, manufacture, importation, use, offering for sale, or selling the LICENSED PRODUCTS in respect of the LICENSED PATENTS (but not other changed or incorporated technology or "design-arounds" of other technologies) contemplated under this AGREEMENT.

**10.3 Mitigation.** Both PARTIES agree to take such reasonable steps to mitigate damages as may be required by the other PARTY.

**10.4 Notice.** The indemnified PARTY will promptly notify the other PARTY of a claim or action in manner to permit adequate defense of the claim or action. The indemnifying PARTY will have the right to control the defense, but both PARTIES will cooperate reasonably in the defense of any such claim or action.

## 11 Assignment

**11.1 LICENSOR Assignees.** This AGREEMENT shall inure to the benefit and be binding on any assignees of LICENSOR.

**11.2 LICENSEE Assignees.** LICENSEE may not transfer any of its rights or obligations under this AGREEMENT without the prior written consent of LICENSOR whether by operation of law or otherwise; provided however, that LICENSEE may assign its rights and/or obligations under this AGREEMENT: (1) To subcontractors as otherwise provided in this AGREEMENT; and (2) to any successor who acquires all or substantially all of the assets of LICENSEE, or who is the survivor of a merger or other corporate reorganization of LICENSEE, without LICENSOR's written consent.

## 12. Term

**12.1 Term.** This AGREEMENT shall begin on the EFFECTIVE DATE and shall endure and remain in full force until the LICENSOR PATENT RIGHTS expire or are abandoned by LICENSOR or are held invalid or unenforceable by a court or governmental entity of competent jurisdiction, unless this AGREEMENT is otherwise earlier terminated pursuant to Paragraphs 12.2, 12.3, or 12.4 of this AGREEMENT, or as otherwise provided herein (the "TERM"). For avoidance of doubt, if US Patent Application No. _____________ and US Patent Application No. ____________ never issue as valid patents or the foregoing applications are amended such that the issued patent claims do not cover the products sold by LICENSEE, and there are no other valid and enforceable patents owned by LICENSOR that cover the products sold by LICENSEE, then this AGREEMENT shall terminate and LICENSOR shall refund any and all royalty amounts paid by LICENSEE to LICENSOR prior to such termination.

**12.2 Termination for Breach.** Either PARTY may terminate this AGREEMENT and the licenses granted herein if the other PARTY is in material breach of this AGREEMENT, after providing written notice to the other PARTY of such intent and reason for termination, provided that the other PARTY shall have thirty (30) calendar days after receipt of such written notice to take prudent and reasonable steps to cure the material breach. Should the other PARTY fail to cure the material breach within the thirty (30) calendar day period, the termination shall become effective.

**12.3 Immediate Right of Termination by LICENSOR.** LICENSOR will have the right to terminate this Agreement immediately by giving written notice to LICENSEE in the event that LICENSEE does any of the following:

- **a.** Fails to obtain or maintain product liability insurance in the amount and of the type provided for herein;
- **b.** Files a petition in bankruptcy or is adjudicated a bankrupt or insolvent, or makes an assignment for the benefit of creditors or an arrangement pursuant to any bankruptcy law, or if the LICENSEE discontinues or dissolves its business or if a receiver is appointed for LICENSEE or for LICENSEE's business and such receiver is not discharged within twenty days;
- **c.** Fails to commence the shipment of Licensed Products within twelve (12) months from the EFFECTIVE DATE of this AGREEMENT; or
- **d.** Upon the commencement of sale of Licensed Products, fails to sell at least [_______________] Licensed Products for two (2) or more consecutive Royalty Periods.

**12.4 Termination without Cause.** Notwithstanding the other provisions of this AGREEMENT, this AGREEMENT shall be subject to termination by LICENSEE upon one hundred twenty (120) days' prior written notice to LICENSOR.

**12.5 Post Termination Obligations.** Upon expiration or termination of this Agreement, LICENSEE will thereafter immediately, except for reason of termination because of expiration or a declaration of patent invalidity, cease all further use of the LICENSED PATENTS and all rights granted to LICENSEE, including its sub-licensees under this Agreement, will forthwith terminate and immediately revert to LICENSOR. In no event will LICENSOR be liable to LICENSEE because of such termination for compensation, reimbursement or damages on account of the loss of prospective profits or anticipated sales, or on account of expenditures, investments, lease, or commitments in connection with the business or good will of LICENSEE. All Royalty obligations will be accelerated and will be immediately due and payable.

13. <u>Manufacture and Quality</u>

**13.1** LICENSEE shall be responsible for all costs of the manufacture, production, marketing, and distribution of the LICENSED PRODUCTS. Any covenant herein by LICENSOR will not be construed or implied to warrant and represent that products made under the LICENSED PATENTS will meet any safety, performance, or other standards, whether imposed by any instrumentality of government or otherwise. All LICENSED PRODUCTS sold will be of a quality commensurate with LICENSEE'S other (type of product) products.

**13.2** LICENSEE will assert no responsibility, and LICENSOR accepts no responsibility or liability for, the noncompliance of LICENSEE or its contract manufacturers with any applicable laws and regulations.

**13.3 Insurance.** LICENSEE will, throughout the TERM of this AGREEMENT, obtain and maintain at its own cost and expense from a qualified insurance company standard Product Liability Insurance with respect to LICENSED PRODUCTS. Such policy will provide protection against all claims, demands, and causes of action arising out of any defects or failure to perform, alleged or otherwise, of the LICENSED PRODUCTS or any material used in connection therewith or any use thereof. The amount of coverage shall be as specified in Schedule A attached. The policy shall provide for 30 days' notice to LICENSOR from the insurer by registered or certified mail, return receipt requested, in the event of any modification, cancellation, or termination. LICENSEE agrees to furnish LICENSOR a certificate of insurance evidencing same on request.

## 14. Miscellaneous

**14.1 Governing Law.** This AGREEMENT shall be governed by the laws of the State of ___________, United States of America, without giving effect to the conflict of laws principles thereof. Anything contained in this Agreement to the contrary notwithstanding, the obligations of the PARTIES and AFFILIATES are subject to all laws, present and future and including export control laws and regulations, of any government having jurisdiction over the PARTIES and AFFILIATES, and to orders, regulations, directions, or requests of any such government. Each PARTY will undertake to comply with and be solely responsible for complying with such laws applicable to such PARTY.

**14.2 Entire AGREEMENT.** This AGREEMENT contains the entire understanding of the PARTIES with respect to the subject matter herein contained and supersedes all previous written or verbal agreements relating to this subject matter between the PARTIES. The PARTIES may, from time to time during the continuance of the AGREEMENT, modify any of the provisions of the AGREEMENT, but only by an instrument in writing duly agreed to and executed by authorized representatives of the PARTIES.

**14.3 Force Majeure.** Neither LICENSOR nor LICENSEE shall be liable to the other for any failure to comply with any terms of the AGREEMENT to the extent any such failure is caused directly or indirectly by fire, strike, union disturbance, injunction or other labor problems, war (whether or not declared), riots, insurrection, government restrictions or other government acts, or other causes beyond the control of or without fault on the part of either LICENSOR or LICENSEE. However, LICENSEE shall continue to be obligated to pay LICENSOR when due any and all amounts which it shall have duly become obligated to pay in accordance with the terms of this AGREEMENT and LICENSOR shall continue to be bound to the exclusivity provisions hereunder. Upon the occurrence of any event of the type referred to in this Paragraph 14.3, the PARTY affected thereby shall give prompt notice thereof to the other PARTY, together with a description of such event and the duration for which such PARTY expects its ability to comply with the provisions of this AGREEMENT to be affected thereby. The PARTY affected shall thereafter devote its best efforts to remedy to the extent possible the condition giving rise to such event and to resume performance of its obligations hereunder as promptly as possible.

**14.4 Further Instruments and Acts.** The PARTIES agree to execute, acknowledge, and deliver all such further instruments, and to do all such other acts as may be necessary and appropriate in order to effectuate the licenses contemplated by this AGREEMENT.

**14.5 Headings.** The headings, section captions, or titles of sections or paragraphs appearing in this AGREEMENT are provided for convenience and are not to be used in construing this AGREEMENT.

**14.6 No Waiver.** No waiver by either PARTY of any default of the other PARTY under this AGREEMENT shall operate or be construed as a waiver of any future defaults, whether of a like or different character. No granting of time or other forbearance or indulgence by either PARTY to the other PARTY shall in any way release, discharge, or otherwise affect the liability of the other PARTY under this AGREEMENT.

**14.7 Notices.** Any notice required or permitted to be given hereunder shall be in the English language and transmitted via the following: facsimile (with confirmation copy mailed afterward), express delivery (e.g., Federal Express), registered mail, or hand delivery. Any such notice shall be deemed to have been delivered on the date of its receipt. All such notices shall be sent to the respective PARTIES at the following addresses:

To LICENSOR:

Company name and address

Attn: ________________

With a copy to: (usually your attorney)

To LICENSEE:

With a copy to: (attorney)

**14.8 Press Releases.** Unless required by applicable law, regulation, or judicial rule, neither PARTY shall issue a press release or other publication regarding any aspect of this AGREEMENT, including any general statements as to the existence of a relationship between the PARTIES, without the prior written consent of the other PARTY.

**14.9 Severability.** The illegality or partial illegality of any or all of this AGREEMENT, or any provision thereof, shall not affect the validity of the remainder of the AGREEMENT, or any such provision thereof, and the illegality or partial illegality of the AGREEMENT or provision thereof shall not affect the validity of the AGREEMENT or provision thereof in any jurisdiction in which such determination of illegality or partial illegality has not been made. In the event of invalidity or partial invalidity of this AGREEMENT or a provision thereof, the PARTIES shall conduct good faith negotiations directed toward mutually agreeable and legally acceptable modifications which reflect the original intent of the PARTIES as of the EFFECTIVE DATE.

**14.10 Disputes.** It is the intention of both PARTIES to attempt to settle all issues by good faith negotiations. However, should such efforts not be successful, all disputes shall be brought exclusively before the appropriate courts in the State of ____________.

**14.11 Relationship between the PARTIES.** This AGREEMENT does not constitute LICENSEE as the agent or legal representative of LICENSOR, or LICENSOR as the agent or legal representative of LICENSEE for any purpose whatsoever. LICENSEE is not granted any right or authority to assume or to create any obligation or responsibility, expressed or implied, on behalf of or in the name of LICENSOR or to bind LICENSOR in any manner or thing whatsoever; nor is LICENSOR granted any right or authority to assume or create any obligation or responsibility, expressed or implied, on behalf of or in the name of LICENSEE or to bind LICENSEE in any manner or thing whatsoever. No joint venture or partnership between LICENSEE and LICENSOR is intended or shall be inferred.

**14.12 Counterparts.** This AGREEMENT may be executed in counterparts, each of which shall be deemed to constitute an original, but all of which together shall constitute one and the same instrument.

**14.13 Non-reliance.** In evaluating and entering into this AGREEMENT, neither LICENSOR nor LICENSEE relied and are relying on any representations, warranties, or other statements, whether oral or written, of the other, except those representations and warranties specifically set forth in this AGREEMENT.

**14.14 Agreement Negotiated.** The form of this AGREEMENT has been negotiated by or on behalf of LICENSEE and LICENSOR, each of who have carefully negotiated the provisions hereof. Each PARTY acknowledges that it has been advised to, and has had the opportunity to, consult with its attorney prior to entering into this AGREEMENT. No law or rule relating to the construction or interpretation of contracts against the drafter of any particular clause should be applied with respect to this AGREEMENT.

**14.15 Fees and Expenses.** Except as specifically provided to the contrary in this AGREEMENT, all costs and expenses incurred in connection with this AGREEMENT shall be paid by the PARTY incurring such expenses.



This AGREEMENT is hereby executed by the PARTIES by their duly authorized representatives.

**AGREED TO AND ACCEPTED:**

By: (Licensee)

___________________________

Its: _____________________

Date: ___________________

By: (Licensor)

___________________________

Its: _____________________

Date: ___________________

**SCHEDULE A**

**A.1** LICENSED PRODUCTS means a _________________manufactured for the MARKET in the TERRITORY, together with any LICENSEE- or LICENSEE AFFILIATE–manufactured or distributed accessories enabling the consumer to use or store the (product) sold together with the _______________ or as after-market _______________ accessories, including ___________,

**A.2** GUARANTEED MINIMUM ROYALTY:

**A.3** INITIAL LICENSE FEE (sometimes an up-front fee is paid in addition to royalties):

# Acknowledgments

**WRITING THIS BOOK** was the easy part. I had no idea of the steps and varied talents needed to bring it to publication.

Thanks to Maria Gagliano for firm but kind editing and then for guiding me and managing the steps and talents needed for proofreading, cover design, book layout design, copywriting, and the list goes on. Thank you to my published author friend Bill Kuhn, who led me to Maria.

I owe thanks to other advisors earlier in the writing process for their assistance: Andi Cumbo-Floyd for an early read and writing suggestions and Kelly Figueroa-Ray for her detailed work on permissions and citations review and edit suggestions.

Thank you all.

# Bibliography

ABC News, "Making Millions Off a Super Mop." March 21, 2006. https://abcnews.go.com/2020/story?id=1782048&page=1.
"About Stephen," InventRight. https://www.inventright.com/about/about-stephen.
Allen, James. *As A Man Thinketh*. 1903.
Arciszewski, Tomasz. *Inventive Engineering: Knowledge and Skills for Creative Engineers*. Boca Raton, FL: CRC Press, 2016.
Baer, Drake. "How Dalí, Einstein and Aristotle Perfected the Power Nap." *Fast Company*, December 10, 2013. https://www.fastcompany.com/3023078/how-dali-einstein-and-aristotle-perfected-the-power-nap.
Bastone, Kelly. "A Brief History of the Sports Bra." *Runner's World*, August 30, 2017.
Belfiore, Michael. "This Cracker-Size Sensor Can Tell You Which Oven Burner You Left On." *Businessweek*, September 18, 2017.
Belsky, Scott. *Making Ideas Happen: Overcoming the Obstacles Between Vision and Reality*. New York: Portfolio, 2010.
Bertagnoli, Lisa. "Neat Trick: Patenting Her Way to Wealth." *Crain's Chicago Business*, September 26, 2009.
Brayer, Elizabeth. *George Eastman: A Biography*. Baltimore: Johns Hopkins University Press, 2006.
Buzan, Tony. *How to Mind Map: The Thinking Tool That Will Change Your Life*. London: Thorsons, 2002.
Carlson, W. Bernard. "Invention and Evolution: The Case of Edison's Sketches of the Telephone," in *Technological Innovation as an Evolutionary Process*, edited by Jon Ziman. New York: Cambridge University Press, 2000, pp. 137–158.
—. *Tesla: Inventor of the Electrical Age*. Princeton, NJ: Princeton University Press, 2013.
Coelho, Paulo. *The Alchemist*. New York: Harper Torch, 1993.
Collier, Peter, and David Horowitz. *The Fords: An American Epic*. San Francisco: Encounter Books, 2002.
Coué, Émile. *Self Mastery Through Conscious Autosuggestion*. New York: Malkan, 1922.
Doyle, Arthur Conan. "A Scandal in Bohemia," *The Adventures of Sherlock Holmes*. London: George Newnes, 1892.
—. *A Study in Scarlet*. London: Ward, Lock & Company, 1887.
—. *Sherlock Holmes: The Complete Novels and Stories*, Vol. 1 and 2. New York: Bantam Dell, 2003.
—. "The Five Orange Pips." *The Adventures of Sherlock Holmes*. London: George Newnes, 1892.
—. "The Boscombe Valley Mystery," *The Adventures of Sherlock Holmes*. London: George Newnes, 1892.

—. "The Adventure of the Cooper Beeches." *The Adventures of Sherlock Holmes*. London: George Newnes, 1892.

Edwards, Betty. *Drawing on the Right Side of the Brain*. New York: TarcherPerigee, 2012.

*Encyclopaedia Britannica*. "Joseph Jenks." https://www.britannica.com/biography/Joseph-Jenks.

Evans, Harold. *They Made America: From the Steam Engine to the Search Engine: Two Centuries of Innovators*. New York: Little, Brown and Company, 2004.

Fenster, J. M. "The Woman Who Invented the Dishwasher." *Invention & Technology* 15, no. 2 (Fall 1999).

Garfield, Simon. *Mauve: How One Man Invented a Color That Changed the World*. London: Faber and Faber, 2000.

Gelb, Michael J. *How to Think Like Leonardo da Vinci: Seven Steps to Genius Every Day*. New York: Dell, 1998.

Gertner, Jon. *The Idea Factory: Bell Labs and the Great Age of American Innovation*. New York: Penguin, 2012.

Gladwell, Malcolm. *Outliers: The Story of Success*. New York: Little, Brown and Company, 2008.

Gorman, Michael E., Matthew E. Mehalik, W. Bernard Carlson, and Michael Oblon, "Alexander Graham Bell, Elisha Gray and the Speaking Telegraph: A Cognitive Comparison," in *History of Technology*, vol. 15, edited by Frank James and Graham Hollister-Short. London: Bloomsbury, 1993: 1–56.

Gray, Charlotte. *Reluctant Genius: Alexander Graham Bell and the Passion for Invention*. New York: Arcade, 2006.

Greiner, Lori. *Invent It, Sell It, Bank It!: Make Your Million-Dollar Idea into a Reality*. New York: Ballantine, 2014.

Grimes, William. "Artur Fischer, Inventor with More Patents Than Edison, Dies at 96." *New York Times*, February 8, 2016.

Hill, Napoleon. *Think & Grow Rich*. Meriden, CT: The Ralston Society, 1937.

Ho, Trang. "Joy Mangano Cleans Up in Sales." *Investor's Daily Business*, July 19, 2010.

Isaacson, Walter. *Einstein: His Life and Universe*. New York: Simon & Schuster, 2007.

—. "The Light-Beam Rider." *New York Times*, November 1, 2015.

James, William. *Principles of Psychology*. New York: Henry Holt and Company, 1890.

Jones, Charlotte Foltz. *Accidents May Happen: Fifty Inventions Discovered by Mistake*. New York: Bantam Doubleday Dell, 1996.

Kanter, Rosabeth Moss, John Kao, and Fred Wiersema. *Innovation: Breakthrough Thinking at 3M, DuPont, GE, Pfizer, and Rubbermaid* (BusinessMasters Series). New York: Harper Business, 1997.

Kassar, Ami. "The Queen of QVC Talks About the Risks of Dealing with Sharks." *New York Times*, October 12, 2012.

Keen, Cathy. "The First Jogbra Was Made by Sewing Together Two Men's Athletic Supporters." Smithsonian.com, April 13, 2015.

Kelley, Tom, and Jonathan Littman. *The Art of Innovation: Lessons in Creativity from IDEO, America's Leading Design Firm*. New York: Currency, 2001.

Kellogg, Richard L. "Sherlock Holmes and the Educational Process," *Teaching of Psychology* 7, no. 1 (1980): 41–44.

Kemper, Steve. *Code Name Ginger: The Story Behind Segway and Dean Kamen's Quest to Invent a New World*. Boston: Harvard Business Review Press, 2003.

Key, Stephen. *One Simple Idea: Turn Your Dreams into a Licensing Goldmine While Letting Others Do the Work*. New York: McGraw-Hill, 2011.

Knight, Will. "The Dark Secret at the Heart of AI." *MIT Technology Review* 120, no. 3 (May/June 2017).

Konig, Susan. "Cleaning Up in Business, With a Mop." *New York Times*, February 11, 2001.

LinkedIn. "Stephen Key." https://www.linkedin.com/in/stephenmkey.

Mangano, Joy, and Alex Tresniowski. *Inventing Joy: Dare to Build a Brace and Creative Life*. New York: Simon & Schuster, 2017.

Mason, Fergus. *Joy: The Unofficial Biography of Miracle Mop Inventor, Joy Mangano*. Anaheim, CA: BookCaps Study Guides, 2015.

McNearney, Allison. "Cinderella Without a Prince." *New York Times*, December 14, 2015.

Michalko, Michael. *ThinkerToys: A Handbook of Creative-Thinking Techniques*. New York: Ten Speed Press, 2006.

Mokyr, Joel. *The Lever of Riches: Technological Creativity and Economic Progress*. New York: Oxford University Press, 1990.

Murphy, Joseph. *The Power of Your Subconscious Mind*. New York: Prentice Hall Press, 2008.

Osborn, Alex Faickney. *Applied Imagination*. New York: Charles Scribner's Sons, 1953.

Pink, Daniel H. *A Whole New Mind: Moving from the Information Age to the Conceptual Age*. New York: Riverhead, 2005.

Robehmed, Natalie. *5 Lessons for Female Entrepreneurs from Shark Tank's Lori Greiner*. Forbes.com, July 24, 2012.

Schwartz, Evan I. *Juice: The Creative Fuel That Drives World-Class Inventors*. Boston: Harvard Business Review Press, 2004.

—. *The Last Lone Inventor: A Tale of Genius, Deceit, and the Birth of Television*. New York: Harper, 2002.

Sherlock, V. M. *The Fever Man: A Biography of Dr. John Gorrie*. Medallion Press, 1982.

Skrabec Jr., Quentin R. *George Westinghouse: Gentle Genius*. New York: Algora Publishing, 2007.

Smith, David J. *If . . . : A Mind-Bending New Way of Looking at Big Ideas and Numbers*. Toronto: Kids Can Press, 2014.

Tan, Siang Yong, and Yvonne Tatsumura. "Alexander Fleming (1881–1955): Discoverer of Penicillin." *Singapore Medical Journal* 56, no. 7 (July 2015): 366–367.

Trickey, Keith V. "The Walt Disney Strategy: The Walt Disney Creative Strategy." http://www.hussted.dk/bibliotek/DisneyPaper.pdf.

Twain, Mark. *Mark Twain's Own Autobiography: The Chapters from the* North Atlantic Review. Madison, WI: University of Wisconsin Press, 1990.

Waitley, Denis E. *Seeds of Greatness: The Ten Best Kept Secrets of Total Success*. Fleming H. Revell Co., 1983.

—. *The Winner's Edge: How to Develop the Critical Attitude for Success*. New York: Times Books, 1980.

Weisman, Aly. "A Grueling 22-Hour Workday in the Life of a QVC Host and 'Shark Tank' Judge." *Business Insider*, April 23, 2012.

Wikipedia. "Alexander Fleming." https://en.wikipedia.org/wiki/Alexander_Fleming.

—. "Joy Mangano." https://en.wifipedia.org/wiki/Joy_Mangano.

—.
"Samuel
Hopkins (inventor)." https://en.wikipedia.org/wike/Samuel_Hopkins_(inventor).
—. "Sports Bra." https://wikipedia.org/wiki/Sports_bra.
Williams, David K. "Lori Greiner, Shark Tank Star and Queen of QVC, on a Great Asset: A Partner in Her Spouse." *Forbes*, September 22, 2012.
Young, James Webb. *A Technique for Producing Ideas*. 1940.

# Index

*Note: Page numbers in italics indicate figures.*

# About the Author

**MICHAEL G. COLBURN** has spent more than 45 years founding and running businesses based on creativity and design. He is most proud of the fact that former key employees purchased and still run some of these businesses or have founded their own. In 2005, he and his wife, Mary Esther Treat, launched Ideas Well Done, a firm that focuses exclusively on inventing new products and bringing them to the marketplace. Since then, Michael has created over 25 inventions and has patents issued in multiple countries.

Ideas Well Done was sold to longtime employee Steve Bogner in 2013 and is still thriving today.

Michael and Mary Esther live in Vermont and enjoy being close to family, cross-country skiing in winter, and long-distance walking in summer and spring.

CPSIA information can be obtained
at www.ICGtesting.com
Printed in the USA
LVHW022229230819
628750LV00028BA/517